The definitive guide to the leading employers recruiting graduates during 2021-2022.

HIGH FLIERS PUBLICATIONS LTD
IN ASSOCIATION WITH THE TIMES

Published by High Fliers Publications Limited
The Gridiron Building, 1 Pancras Square, London, N1C 4AG
Telephone: 020 7428 9100   *Web:* www.Top100GraduateEmployers.com

Editor Martin Birchall
Publisher Gill Thomas
Production Manager Jeremy Brown
Photographers Nevra Topcu, Charlotte Elcock
Distribution Manager Louis Elston

The Times Top 100 Graduate Employers is based on research
results from *The UK Graduate Careers Survey 2021,*
produced by High Fliers Research Ltd.

The greatest care has been taken in compiling this book.
However, no responsibility can be accepted by the publishers
or compilers for the accuracy of the information presented.

Where opinion is expressed it is that of the author or advertiser
and does not necessarily coincide with the editorial views of
High Fliers Publications Limited or *The Times* newspaper.

Printed and bound in Italy by L.E.G.O. S.p.A.

A CIP catalogue record for this book
is available from the British Library.
ISBN 978-1-9160401-2-0

Contents

Foreword

By **Martin Birchall**
Editor, *The Times Top 100 Graduate Employers*

Welcome to the 2021-2022 edition of *The Times Top 100 Graduate Employers*, your annual guide to the UK's most prestigious and sought-after graduate employers.

Standing in the leafy central courtyard of AstraZeneca's futuristic new research & development centre on the Cambridge Biomedical Campus, there are few signs of the company's huge effort to deliver up to three billion doses of its COVID-19 vaccine across the globe by the end of 2021.

AstraZeneca partnered with the University of Oxford in April 2020 to develop and manufacture the vaccine, and it is now being produced at 25 manufacturing sites in 15 countries.

Its work on the vaccine has helped AstraZeneca become one of the world's most recognisable companies and has increased its popularity as a graduate employer too. AstraZeneca is amongst this year's highest-climbers in *The Times Top 100 Graduate Employers* and has reached the top twenty in the rankings for the first time.

Thankfully, the successful rollout of COVID-19 vaccines has enabled the UK to open up very substantially after three national lockdowns and months of social distancing, mask-wearing, testing and travel restrictions during the pandemic.

University life during the 2020-2021 academic year was almost unrecognisable – with lectures and exams switched online, little or no face-to-face teaching, reduced access to campuses, and social 'bubbles' for students living in university accommodation.

Graduate job hunting was very different too. The country's best-known employers promoted their graduate vacancies through virtual careers fairs and online presentations rather than their usual programme of on-campus promotions, and moved to fully online selection and assessment for all of their graduate recruitment.

Final year students who left university in the summer of 2021 found themselves competing with tens of thousands of graduates from the previous year who had struggled during the pandemic to find a graduate job after university.

And, despite making many more job applications than ever before, the proportion of final year students who secured a graduate job offer before leaving university dropped by a third, and confidence in the graduate employment market fell to an all-time low.

One in six students abandoned job hunting altogether because of their mental health, and a record number of finalists opted for postgraduate study rather than applying for a graduate job.

Although some students found the new era of online recruitment more convenient, over half of students from the 'Class of 2021' said it had been

" AstraZeneca is amongst this year's highest-climbers in the Top 100 and has reached the top twenty for the first time. "

harder to find out which employers were offering graduate vacancies, and a third complained that it had been more difficult to have one-to-one conversations with recruiters or recent graduates.

It's encouraging that the majority of employers listed in *The Times Top 100 Graduate Employers* have been able to maintain their graduate programmes and have carried on recruiting throughout the pandemic. From the City's investment banks and top accounting & professional services firms to well-known technology companies and elite international law firms, the country's leading employers have continued to invest in the graduates that their organisations need for the future.

It isn't clear when employers will be able to return to universities to publicise their work experience opportunities and graduate vacancies for 2022. Few campus careers fairs will be able to take place during the autumn, and most graduate employers expect to hold their recruitment presentations online, rather than in person at universities, in the first part of the 2021-2022 academic year.

But the good news is that the number of graduate vacancies available at the UK's top employers increased in 2021 – following the sharp drop

in graduate recruitment at the beginning of the Coronavirus crisis – and is expected to rise again in 2022 as the country continues to recover from the pandemic.

The editorial features in this edition examine how the Coronavirus pandemic has affected the graduate job market and the individual employers featured in *The Times Top 100 Graduate Employers*, as well as the improving prospects for university-leavers in the year ahead.

Since the first edition was published in 1999, more than a million copies of *The Times Top 100 Graduate Employers* have now been produced, helping students and graduates at universities across the UK to research their career options and find their first graduate job. More than two decades on, the *Top 100* continues to provide an unrivalled, independent assessment of the country's most highly rated graduate employers.

The Times Top 100 Graduate Employers will not necessarily identify which organisation you should join after graduation – only you can decide that. But it is an invaluable reference, especially in such uncertain times, if you want to discover what the UK's leading employers are offering for new graduates in 2022.

THE TIMES TOP 100 GRADUATE EMPLOYERS — Finding out about the Top 100 Graduate Employers

PRINT & DIGITAL EDITION

Each employer featured in this edition of the *Top 100* has their own **Employer Entry**, providing details of graduate vacancies for 2022, minimum academic requirements, starting salaries, for new graduates, plus this year's application deadlines.

WEBSITE

Register now with the official *Top 100* website for full access to the very latest information about the UK's most sought-after graduate employers.

This includes details of employers' internships & work experience programmes, local university promotions and application deadlines.

And get ready for your applications, online interviews and assessment centres with up-to-the-minute business news about each of the organisations featured in this year's *Top 100*.

www.Top100GraduateEmployers.com

BY EMAIL

Once you've registered with the *Top 100* website, you'll receive **weekly email bulletins** with news of the employers you're interested in, details of their latest graduate vacancies, and their forthcoming application deadlines.

Explore. Inspire.

Reimagine.

At PwC, we're building a diverse
community and championing greater
flexibility, so everyone can feel like
they belong.

We're looking for inspired minds; whether
you're designing and implementing digital
audit programmes, helping clients navigate
a more complex tax world, or providing
strategic consulting advice, we'll prepare
you for the future, powered by the latest
technology. We work together to deliver
sustainable outcomes and responsible
growth for our clients and our communities.

Find where you belong.

Visit here to find out more:

pwc.co.uk/careers

f **PwCCareersUK** | **in** **pwc-uk**

○ **pwc_uk_careers** | **▶** **PwC UK Careers**

🐦 **@pwc_uk_careers**

Valuing Difference. Driving Inclusion.

pwc

#TeamAldi

2021/22
UK
300

THE TIMES — TOP 100 GRADUATE EMPLOYERS — 2013-2014

THE TIMES — TOP 100 GRADUATE EMPLOYERS — 2014-2015

THE TIMES — TOP 100 GRADUATE EMPLOYERS — 2015-2016

THE TIMES — TOP 100 GRADUATE EMPLOYERS — 2016-2017

THE TIMES — TOP 100 GRADUATE EMPLOYERS — 2017-2018

THE TIMES — TOP 100 GRADUATE EMPLOYERS — 2018-2019

THE TIMES — TOP 100 GRADUATE EMPLOYERS — 2019-2020

THE TIMES — TOP 100 GRADUATE EMPLOYERS — 2020-2021

THE TIMES — TOP 100 GRADUATE EMPLOYERS — 2021-2022

Researching The Times Top 100 Graduate Employers

By **Gill Thomas**
Publisher, High Fliers Publications

There were an estimated 5,000 employers, large and small, recruiting graduates from UK universities when the first edition of *The Times Top 100 Graduate Employers* was published in 1999.

The number of graduate employers has risen steadily over the past two decades and, before the onset of the Coronavirus pandemic, there were at least 200,000 graduate-level vacancies available annually.

For university students researching their career options, finding the 'right' graduate employer can often be a daunting prospect. What basis can you use to evaluate such a large number of organisations and the opportunities they offer for graduates after university?

The Times Top 100 Graduate Employers is compiled annually by the independent market research company, High Fliers Research, through interviews with final year students at the country's leading universities.

This latest edition is based on research with 16,121 students who were due to graduate from universities across the UK in the summer of 2021. It was completed in the second half of February 2021 via Zoom interviews, in the middle of the country's third national lockdown of the pandemic.

Final year students from the 'Class of 2021' who took part in the study were selected at random to represent the full cross-section of finalists at their universities, not just those who had already secured graduate employment. The research examined students' experiences during their search for a first graduate job and asked them about their attitudes to employers.

The question used to produce the *Top 100* rankings was "Which employer do you think offers the best opportunities for graduates?". The question was deliberately open-ended and students were not shown a list of employers to choose from or prompted during the interview.

The wide selection of answers given during the research shows that final year students used very different criteria to decide which employer offered the best opportunities for graduates. Some evaluated employers based on the quality of the recruitment promotions they'd seen whilst at university – either online or in-person – or their recent experiences during the application and graduate selection process.

Other final year students used the 'graduate employment proposition' as their main guide – the quality of training and development an employer offers, the starting salary and remuneration package available, and the practical aspects of a first graduate job, such as its location or the likely working hours.

" For the third year running, the Civil Service is named the UK's number one graduate employer within the new rankings. "

THE TIMES TOP 100 GRADUATE EMPLOYERS
The Times Top 100 Graduate Employers 2021

	2020			2020	
1	1	CIVIL SERVICE	51	36	UNLOCKED
2	2	PWC	52	59	BAKER MCKENZIE
3	4	NHS	53	44	DLA PIPER
4	3	DELOITTE	54	51	ROYAL NAVY
5	5	ALDI	55	52	AECOM
6	12	EY	56	76	CITI
7	6	GOOGLE	57	64	DEUTSCHE BANK
8	9	BBC	58	NEW	ITV
9	8	TEACH FIRST	59	78	UBS
10	7	KPMG	60	61	WHITE & CASE
11	11	GSK	61	55	HERBERT SMITH FREEHILLS
12	10	J.P. MORGAN	62	54	APPLE
13	14	HSBC	63	57	BLOOMBERG
14	17	AMAZON	64	41	DYSON
15	15	BARCLAYS	65	53	ATKINS
16	13	UNILEVER	66	85	SAVILLS
17	16	GOLDMAN SACHS	67	NEW	NESTLÉ
18	34	P&G	68	69	BLACKROCK
19	26	LINKLATERS	69	45	AIRBUS
20	56	ASTRAZENECA	70	87	TPP
21	49	L'ORÉAL	71	60	VODAFONE
22	21	MCKINSEY & COMPANY	72	NEW	THG
23	23	ARMY	73	NEW	RED BULL
24	28	ARUP	74	67	BAIN & COMPANY
25	24	CLIFFORD CHANCE	75	80	MCDONALD'S
26	19	ROLLS-ROYCE	76	NEW	PFIZER
27	38	ALLEN & OVERY	77	89	GCHQ
28	29	POLICE NOW	78	NEW	IRWIN MITCHELL
29	31	BAE SYSTEMS	79	47	MI5
30	20	ACCENTURE	80	70	FRESHFIELDS BRUCKHAUS DERINGER
31	50	PENGUIN RANDOM HOUSE	81	82	WELLCOME
32	37	FRONTLINE	82	58	MARS
33	30	SKY	83	75	CMS
34	25	IBM	84	99	HOGAN LOVELLS
35	48	BT	85	NEW	ARM
36	18	LIDL	86	NEW	BANK OF AMERICA
37	33	NATWEST GROUP	87	NEW	KUBRICK
38	46	BOSTON CONSULTING GROUP	88	92	GRANT THORNTON
39	40	THINK AHEAD	89	NEW	THE WALT DISNEY COMPANY
40	32	LLOYDS BANKING GROUP	90	42	SHELL
41	62	TESCO	91	98	BANK OF ENGLAND
42	35	BP	92	NEW	PEPSICO
43	88	CHARITYWORKS	93	39	JAGUAR LAND ROVER
44	22	NEWTON	94	95	MOTT MACDONALD
45	43	MORGAN STANLEY	95	73	ENTERPRISE
46	66	SLAUGHTER AND MAY	96	81	SIEMENS
47	27	MICROSOFT	97	NEW	RSM
48	77	CHANNEL 4	98	NEW	LATHAM & WATKINS
49	NEW	BDO	99	NEW	MAZARS
50	71	LOCAL GOVERNMENT	100	NEW	DIAGEO

Source **High Fliers Research** 16,121 final year students leaving UK universities in the summer of 2021 were asked the open-ended question "Which employer do you think offers the best opportunities for graduates?" during interviews for *The UK Graduate Careers Survey 2021*

Across the full survey sample, final year students named more than 1,500 different organisations – from new start-up businesses and small local or regional employers, to some of the world's best-known companies. The responses were analysed and the one hundred organisations that were mentioned most often make up *The Times Top 100 Graduate Employers* for 2021.

For the third year running, the Civil Service is named the UK's number one graduate employer within the new rankings. Best known for its prestigious Fast Stream programme, a total of 6.3 per cent of final year students from the 'Class of 2021' voted for the Civil Service, which was more than three hundred votes ahead of the next most popular employer in this year's league table.

PwC, the 'Big Four' accounting & professional services firm that held the number one position for fifteen years until 2018, remains in second place.

After its gruelling year at the frontline of the Coronavirus crisis in the UK, there has been a noticeable increase in votes for the NHS, taking it into the top three in the *Top 100* for the first time, ahead of the professional services firm Deloitte and retailer Aldi.

Having slipped to 12th place in 2020, 'Big Four' firm EY has bounced back to sixth place this year, overtaking rival firm KPMG, which has dropped back to tenth place.

Google and the widely acclaimed Teach First programme slip one place each, but the BBC moves up to eighth position in the new rankings. Amazon delivers its highest position yet, and Procter & Gamble has climbed to its best ranking for eleven years. And, in 19th place, Linklaters is the first law firm to ever be ranked within the top twenty in *The Times Top 100 Graduate Employers*.

The highest climbers in the new *Top 100* are led by the Charityworks programme, which has jumped an impressive forty-five places to 43rd place. AstraZeneca, the pharmaceuticals company that has shot to prominence over the past twelve months with its Coronavirus vaccine, has leapt thirty-six places from outside the top fifty in 2020, to reach 20th place in this year's rankings.

Channel 4, L'Oréal, Tesco and Local Government have each climbed more than twenty places, and there have been similarly big moves for law firm Slaughter and May, banking groups Citi and UBS, publishers Penguin Random House, and Savills – which remains the only property firm to be listed within the *Top 100*.

The biggest fallers of the year include Jaguar Land Rover – which has crashed back fifty-four places from 39th in 2020 to 93rd place this year – and Shell, which has dropped forty-eight places to 90th position. MI5 - the Security Service, consumer goods company Mars, Airbus, Dyson, Enterprise, Newton and Microsoft have each fallen at least twenty places in the new rankings.

There are an unprecedented sixteen new entries or re-entries in this year's league table, marking the most dramatic changeover of employers in the history of *The Times Top 100 Graduate Employers*.

The highest re-entry is accounting & professional services firm BDO, which returns in 49th place, its best-ever ranking. It is joined by the broadcaster ITV, retailer THG (The Hut Group), technology company Arm, Kubrick, The Walt Disney Company, PepsiCo and law firm Latham & Watkins – all of which are ranked for the first time.

Pharmaceuticals company and vaccine producer Pfizer has returned to the *Top 100* for only the second time since 2008, along with Nestlé, Red Bull, law firm Irwin Mitchell, the Bank of America and drinks company Diageo, which are all re-entries in the new *Top 100*.

There are a record eight accounting & professional services firms in this year's rankings, as RSM and Mazars have made their *Top 100* debuts at 97th and 99th places respectively.

Among the sixteen employers leaving the *Top 100* in 2021 are three employers that had appeared in the rankings every year since *The Times Top 100 Graduate Employers* launched in 1999. High street retailers Marks & Spencer and Boots are both former top ten employers from the *Top 100*, and oil & energy company ExxonMobil had previously been ranked as a top twenty graduate employer. And, for only the second time in the last two decades, the RAF isn't ranked as a *Top 100* employer for new graduates.

Other employers that are no longer ranked in this year's league table include Network Rail, online retailer ASOS, law firm Pinsent Masons, global technology companies Huawei and Facebook, insurance company Admiral and six employers that were new or re-entries in the 2020 rankings – Capital One, American Express, Tesla, the Environment Agency, Samsung and BMW.

Since the original edition of *The Times Top 100 Graduate Employers* was published more than two decades ago, just three organisations have made it to number one in the rankings. Andersen

Spreadsheet robot?

THINK YOU KNOW ACCOUNTING?
YOU'RE IN FOR A SURPRISE.

Whatever your degree, it's time to expect
the unexpected with a qualification that opens
doors everywhere. From cars to cosmetics,
ICAEW can take you to more places than you think.

We get you there
icaew.com/careers

Consulting (now Accenture) held on to the top spot for the first four years, and its success heralded a huge surge in popularity for careers in consulting. At its peak in 2001, almost one in six graduates applied for jobs in the sector.

In the year before the firm changed its name from Andersen Consulting to Accenture, it astutely introduced a new graduate package that included a £28,500 starting salary (a sky-high figure for graduates in 2000) and a much-talked-about £10,000 bonus, helping to assure the firm's popularity, irrespective of its corporate branding.

In 2003, after two dismal years in graduate recruitment when vacancies for university-leavers dropped by more than a fifth following the terrorist attacks of 11th September 2001, the Civil Service was named the UK's leading graduate employer.

Just twelve months later it was displaced by PricewaterhouseCoopers, the accounting and professional services firm formed from the merger of Price Waterhouse and Coopers & Lybrand in 1998. At the time, the firm was the largest private sector recruiter of graduates, with an intake in 2004 of more than a thousand trainees.

Now known simply as PwC, the firm remained at number one for an impressive fifteen years, increasing its share of the student vote from 5 per cent in 2004 to more than 10 per cent in 2007, and fighting off the stiffest of competition from rivals Deloitte in 2008, when just seven votes separated the two employers.

PwC's reign as the UK's leading graduate employer represented a real renaissance for the entire accounting & professional services sector. Twenty years ago, a career in accountancy was regarded as a safe, traditional employment choice, whereas today's profession is viewed in a very different light. The training required to become a chartered accountant is now seen as a prized business qualification, and the sector's leading firms are regularly described as 'dynamic' and 'international' by undergraduates looking for their first job after university.

A total of 225 different organisations have now appeared within *The Times Top 100 Graduate Employers* since its inception, and thirty-five of these have made it into the rankings every year since 1999.

The most consistent performers have been PwC, KPMG and the Civil Service, each of which have never been lower than 10th place in the league table. The NHS has also had a formidable record,

THE TIMES TOP 100 GRADUATE EMPLOYERS — Number Ones, Movers & Shakers in the Top 100

NUMBER ONES		HIGHEST CLIMBING EMPLOYERS		HIGHEST NEW ENTRIES	
1999	ANDERSEN CONSULTING	1999	SCHLUMBERGER (UP 13 PLACES)	1999	PFIZER (31st)
2000	ANDERSEN CONSULTING	2000	CAPITAL ONE (UP 32 PLACES)	2000	MORGAN STANLEY (34th)
2001	ACCENTURE	2001	EUROPEAN COMMISSION (UP 36 PLACES)	2001	MARCONI (36th)
2002	ACCENTURE	2002	WPP (UP 36 PLACES)	2002	GUINNESS UDV (44th)
2003	CIVIL SERVICE	2003	ROLLS-ROYCE (UP 37 PLACES)	2003	ASDA (40th)
2004	PRICEWATERHOUSECOOPERS	2004	J.P. MORGAN (UP 29 PLACES)	2004	BAKER & MCKENZIE (61st)
2005	PRICEWATERHOUSECOOPERS	2005	TEACH FIRST (UP 22 PLACES)	2005	PENGUIN (70th)
2006	PRICEWATERHOUSECOOPERS	2006	GOOGLE (UP 32 PLACES)	2006	FUJITSU (81st)
2007	PRICEWATERHOUSECOOPERS	2007	PFIZER (UP 30 PLACES)	2007	BDO STOY HAYWARD (74th)
2008	PRICEWATERHOUSECOOPERS	2008	CO-OPERATIVE GROUP (UP 39 PLACES)	2008	SKY (76th)
2009	PRICEWATERHOUSECOOPERS	2009	CADBURY (UP 48 PLACES)	2009	BDO STOY HAYWARD (68th)
2010	PRICEWATERHOUSECOOPERS	2010	ASDA (UP 41 PLACES)	2010	SAATCHI & SAATCHI (49th)
2011	PWC	2011	CENTRICA (UP 41 PLACES)	2011	APPLE (53rd)
2012	PWC	2012	NESTLÉ (UP 44 PLACES)	2012	EUROPEAN COMMISSION (56th)
2013	PWC	2013	DFID (UP 40 PLACES)	2013	SIEMENS (70th)
2014	PWC	2014	TRANSPORT FOR LONDON (UP 36 PLACES)	2014	FRONTLINE (76th)
2015	PWC	2015	DIAGEO, NEWTON (UP 43 PLACES)	2015	DANONE (66th)
2016	PWC	2016	BANK OF ENGLAND (UP 34 PLACES)	2016	SANTANDER (63rd)
2017	PWC	2017	CANCER RESEARCH UK (UP 38 PLACES)	2017	DYSON (52nd)
2018	PWC	2018	MCDONALD'S (UP 30 PLACES)	2018	ASOS (52nd)
2019	CIVIL SERVICE	2019	POLICE NOW (UP 43 PLACES)	2019	UNLOCKED (49th)
2020	CIVIL SERVICE	2020	DLA PIPER / WHITE & CASE (UP 32 PLACES)	2020	CHANNEL FOUR (77th)
2021	CIVIL SERVICE	2021	CHARITYWORKS (UP 45 PLACES)	2021	BDO (49th)

Source High Fliers Research

appearing in every top ten since 2003, while the BBC, Goldman Sachs and EY (formerly Ernst & Young) have all remained within the top twenty throughout the last decade.

Google is the highest-climbing employer within the *Top 100*, having risen over eighty places during the last decade, to reach the top three for the first time in 2015. But car manufacturer Jaguar Land Rover holds the record for the fastest-moving employer, after jumping more than seventy places in just five years, between 2009 and 2014.

Other employers haven't been so successful. British Airways ranked in 6th place in 1999 but dropped out of the *Top 100* a decade later, and Ford, which was once rated as high as 14th, disappeared out of the list in 2006 after cancelling its graduate recruitment programme two years previously. A more recent high-ranking casualty

is the John Lewis Partnership, which – having been 9th in 2003 – tumbled out of the *Top 100* in 2020.

More than thirty graduate employers – including Nokia, Maersk, the Home Office, Cable & Wireless, United Biscuits, Nationwide, Capgemini and the Met Office – have the dubious record of having only been ranked in the *Top 100* once during the last twenty years. And Marconi had the unusual distinction of being one of the highest-ever new entries, in 36th place in 2001, only to vanish from the list entirely the following year.

One of the most spectacular ascendancies in the *Top 100* has been the rise of Aldi, which joined the list in 65th place in 2002, rose to 3rd place in 2009 – helped in part by its memorable remuneration package for new recruits (currently £44,000 plus a BMW 3 Series car) – and was ranked in 2nd place in both 2015 and 2016.

THE TIMES TOP 100 GRADUATE EMPLOYERS — Winners & Losers in the Top 100

MOST CONSISTENT EMPLOYERS	HIGHEST RANKING	LOWEST RANKING
PWC	1st (2004-2018)	3rd (1999-2001, 2003)
CIVIL SERVICE	1st (2003, 2019-2021)	8th (2011)
KPMG	3rd (2006-2008, 2011-2012)	10th (2021)
BBC	5th (2005-2007)	14th (1999)
GSK	10th (2017-2018)	22nd (2002-2003)
EY (FORMERLY ERNST & YOUNG)	6th (2021)	20th (2001)
GOLDMAN SACHS	5th (2001)	25th (1999)
IBM	13th (2000)	34th (2021)
CLIFFORD CHANCE	24th (2020)	45th (2007)
HSBC	6th (2003)	29th (1999)

EMPLOYERS CLIMBING HIGHEST	NEW ENTRY RANKING	HIGHEST RANKING
GOOGLE	85th (2005)	3rd (2015)
LIDL	89th (2009)	13th (2017)
NEWTON	94th (2013)	19th (2019)
JAGUAR LAND ROVER	87th (2009)	16th (2014)
AMAZON	81st (2015)	14th (2021)
ALDI	65th (2002)	2nd (2015-2016)
MI5 – THE SECURITY SERVICE	96th (2007)	33rd (2010)
POLICE NOW	90th (2018)	28th (2021)
TEACH FIRST	63rd (2003)	2nd (2014)
APPLE	87th (2009)	27th (2012)

EMPLOYERS FALLING FURTHEST	HIGHEST RANKING	LOWEST RANKING
BRITISH AIRWAYS	6th (1999)	Not ranked (2010, 2011, 2017, FROM 2019)
MARKS & SPENCER	7th (1999)	Not ranked (2021)
JOHN LEWIS PARTNERSHIP	9th (2013)	Not ranked (2020)
BOOTS	10th (1999)	Not ranked (2021)
FORD	11th (1999)	Not ranked (FROM 2006)
UBS	17th (2002)	Not ranked (2018)
SAINSBURY'S	18th (2003)	Not ranked (FROM 2016)
EXXONMOBIL	19th (1999)	Not ranked (2021)
SHELL	11th (2006)	90th (2021)
THOMSON REUTERS	22nd (2001)	Not ranked (2009-2012, FROM 2014)

Source High Fliers Research

ICAS

Zahrah Mahmood
Summit-seeking
Chartered Accountant

CALLING ALL TRAILBLAZERS

LAUNCH YOUR CAREER AS A CHARTERED ACCOUNTANT

icas.com/becomeaca

Teach First, the first of five inspirational schemes that are transforming society by bringing top graduates into public service, appeared as a new entry in 63rd place in 2003, before climbing the rankings every year for a decade and reaching 2nd place in the *Top 100* in 2014. Over the last three years another of these programmes, Police Now,

has jumped more than sixty places from 90th in 2018 to 28th place in the latest rankings.

This year's 23rd edition of *The Times Top 100 Graduate Employers* provides a unique insight into how new graduates from the 'Class of 2021' rated the country's leading employers – in the very midst of the Coronavirus pandemic.

THE TIMES TOP 100 GRADUATE EMPLOYERS — The UK's Number 1 Graduate Employer 2021

"To be named number one in *The Times Top 100 Graduate Employers* for the third year in a row is an immense achievement. I'm so proud of what the recruitment team at the Civil Service Fast Stream has achieved in such a challenging year.

The Civil Service Fast Stream has a long and distinguished history of recruiting the leaders of the future for Government departments and the wider Civil Service – in good times and more difficult times too.

The Coronavirus pandemic brought so much change and disruption over the last eighteen months. Yet all of the Fast Streamers we recruited in 2020 were able to start their roles as planned. Many were posted directly into areas that were delivering the Government's critical response to the crisis, like the Department of Health and Social Care or NHS Track and Trace. It was the most pivotal point in a whole generation to be joining the Civil Service. An amazing opportunity for our new Fast Streamers to play their part in supporting the nation during the pandemic.

The pandemic showed the Civil Service's agility to respond to a crisis. For the Fast Stream, we continued with our recruitment in full. We had over 60,000 applications for places on the Fast Stream in 2021.

Assessment centres for the Fast Stream – which before had been face-to-face – moved online. We assessed over 3,500 candidates virtually during the selection process. It was a very significant change and we worked very hard to ensure we continued to provide a positive candidate experience during the assessments.

We're excited to be launching our new 2022 recruitment campaign and will be offering 950 places on fifteen different schemes within the Fast Stream. These include roles in digital,

Sonia Pawson, Head of the Civil Service Fast Stream

data and technology, finance, commercial, science and the Diplomatic Service.

We have a brand-new recruitment website and will have some face-to-face events and activities at universities as well. We'll also be continuing with the fully virtual selection and assessment centres that we pioneered in 2021.

One of the things we've seen from the last year is that more graduates than ever are wanting to make a real difference and contribute to public service. The pandemic has shone a light on so many of the important areas of policy that civil servants are involved in. It has really helped people understand more about what the Civil Service does.

Through our new marketing campaign, we'll be encouraging applications from across the country – and from the broadest possible range of backgrounds – to join the Civil Service Fast Stream in 2022. "

Raise your ambition

Opportunities as extraordinary as you

Week after week you'll build skills and confidence on our graduate programmes and find out what it takes to be part of an operation that feeds the nation.

Careers as extraordinary as you

Scan the QR code to find out more or visit our website:

 lidlgraduatecareers.co.uk

Shaping lives has never been so rewarding.

Teaching is a chance to inspire the next generation and **make a real difference** in children's lives.

In teaching, you start in the classroom – but where you go from there is up to you. **Pastoral roles** provide opportunities to support the next generation to be their best, if you love what you teach you could become a **head of subject**, or with a **leadership role** you could make a real impact within a school – leading, managing, and motivating staff.

Postgraduate teacher training courses are available across England, led by universities or schools. Whichever course you choose, your training will largely be the same, and will usually offer a **postgraduate qualification** like a PGCE.

Search: **Get Into Teaching**

Department
for Education

**Jake Athorn,
History teacher**

**The Redhill
Academy**

"During my time at school my history department were brilliant, as they were able to deliver lessons that were both entertaining and inspiring. By becoming a history teacher, I see it as my duty to give back to pupils what my own history teachers gave to me.

I grew up in Nottingham, which is also incidentally the city I am lucky enough to currently teach in. Nottingham is rich in history with both the legend of Robin Hood and the Civil War remnants being a huge part of our culture. Consequently, it is usually the case that students already have a positive outlook on the subject of history, I look to nurture and enhance this in my lessons.

There is a common thought that the workload for teachers is so large, there is no room to live your life outside of school. I have found quite the contrary and have been able to balance both a hard-working school day with a vibrant social life. I am an avid sportsman and play football and golf around 3 to 4 times a week. Overall, I am incredibly happy I chose teaching as a career. I think both my friends and family would say I am living my life to the fullest extent."

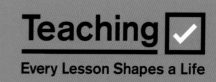

Teaching ✓

Every Lesson Shapes a Life

How the Class of 2021 was sold shor[t]

In a new three-part series, *Helen Chandler-Wilde* meets the out-of-pocket university students who may soon be out of w[ork]

Class of 2021

Part One

T hey were so despe[rate]
they pinned pleas f[rom]
the windows: "SO[S]
"Send food", read anoth[er]
students in Parker Hous[e]

'I feel left behind': graduates struggle to secure good jobs

[cent increase] pride myself on, yet the job market   ties . . . And it's easier to stick to the   'I reckon
                                                       safer, well-paid path than take a risk and   [...]
                                                       [...]hey said

Covid job gloom for graduate[s]

By **Eleanor Busby**

GRADUATES have
struggled to get prop[er]
jobs in the pandemic,
figures reveal.
  The share in full-ti[me]
positions over a year
after university fell fr[om]
[...]r cent.
[...]the 380,970
[...]e Outcome[s]
[...]he Higher
[...]Statistics
[...]re quizzed
[...]pandemic,
[...]onths after
[...]uated.
[...]18-19 group
[...]ed a rise in

Global economy gears up for fastest recovery in 80 years

Richard Partington
Economics correspondent

The global economy is set for the [fast]est recovery from recession for [more] than 80 years, but poor nation[s] risk of falling further behind we[althier] countries amid slow progress [on] the Covid-19 vaccine, the World [Bank] has said.
  In its half-yearly outlook rep[ort] the Washington-based institu[tion] said the world economy was [fore]cast to grow at 5.6% this year, [...]

Graduates jostle in an overcrowded jobs market

University leavers in 2021 are competing for roles   schemes, which means there are potentially many thousands of extra applicants f[or the] limited [number of] [...]

Pay booms as jo[b] vacancies excee[d] pre-Covid levels

EMPLOYMENT
Simon English and Naomi Ackerman

PAY is booming as the jobs market recovers and vacancies go above [pre-pan]demic [leve]ls.

jobs market is moving into a mor[e] [tur]bulent period with unemploy[ment] likely to drift moderately higher [in the] near term as the furlough sch[eme] winds down and those who sto[pped] looking for work during Covid re[turn] [...]ate of unemployment i[s]

Financial hit from Covid far less drastic than feared

[...] [0].4 per cent, from 6.6 per cent to   Tom Waters, an author of th[e] report
[...]

Retail enjoys strongest sales in four years as shoppers return to the high street

The CBI's monthly survey of 117   Inflation has mostly [...]
retail businesses found that compa-   a steep rise in oil pr[...]
[...]erating in the [re]tail, wholesale   [...]owed steep falls las[t]
                                        [...]ckdown. M[...]

Pandemic sparks intere[st] in public sector jobs

[...]d security are

Employers go on hiring spree as economic recovery gathers pace

Philip Aldrick Economics Editor

Employers brought 356,000 people   time, and job vacancies rose to 862,000   picture of a labour market well on its   ment. Three of the sectors that had the
back to work between May and June,   — 77,500 above pre-Covid levels — as   way to recovery".   steepest falls in empl[oyment]
the largest monthly increase   all but one sector experienced an   Y[...] [...]
[...]   increase in rec[...]

Strongest growth in business activity for more than two decades as curbs ease

business confidence. The PMI for   for manufacturers, how[...]

Coronavirus and the Graduate Job Market

By **Martin Birchall**
Managing Director, High Fliers Research

When the UK was plunged into lockdown at the start of the Coronavirus crisis in March 2020, many of the UK's top employers were forced to pause or re-evaluate their graduate recruitment, and many were unable to continue with their planned annual intake of university-leavers.

As a result, the final number of graduates recruited by employers featured in *The Times Top 100 Graduate Employers* in 2020 was a sixth lower than had been originally intended, and over 12 per cent less than in 2019.

Graduate recruitment was cut in thirteen out of fifteen industries and business sectors, most noticeably at the major engineering & industrial companies and the accounting & professional services firms, where over 700 planned vacancies were left unfilled.

This was the most significant annual fall in graduate recruitment since the global financial crisis struck 13 years ago. The recession that followed in the UK in 2008 and 2009 had a very dramatic effect on graduate vacancies, and recruitment dropped by an unprecedented 23 per cent in less than 18 months.

Although the graduate job market bounced back in 2010 with an annual increase in vacancies of more than 12 per cent, it took a further five years

THE TIMES
TOP 100
GRADUATE EMPLOYERS

❝ The outlook for graduate recruitment seems considerably brighter than it did eighteen months ago. ❞

for graduate recruitment to overtake the pre-recession peak recorded in 2007.

By 2019, graduate recruitment was up by 43 per cent compared to the number of vacancies available in 2009 – the low point in the graduate job market during the economic crisis – and it was expected to rise even higher.

The Coronavirus pandemic brought this period of sustained growth to a very abrupt end. But unlike previous economic downturns and recessions, the majority of the country's best-known employers did continue with their graduate recruitment – albeit with fewer places at many organisations – rather than postponing or cutting their entry-level programmes entirely.

Graduate recruitment at the UK's top employers began to make a cautious recovery in 2021, with more entry-level vacancies in sectors such as technology, retail and consulting.

And, having made very significant cuts to their graduate recruitment in 2020, several employers in the engineering & industrial sector needed to step up their next annual intake.

Four well-known employers recruited at least 300 extra graduates in 2021, either because their organisations had under-recruited in the previous year or their business had expanded substantially during the pandemic.

Unleash your potential

We cultivate smart, aspiring, diverse talent to harness the power of data, AI, and cloud technology to helpworld-leading organisations transform.

Shape your tomorrow.
Become a Kubrick Consultant today.

kubrickgroup.com/join-us

Edward Gibbs
Data Management Consultant

Other parts of the graduate job market fared less well, with further reductions in recruitment in banking & finance, at consumer goods companies and in the oil & energy sector. In all, two-fifths of the UK's top graduate employers recruited fewer graduates in 2021 than they had in 2020.

Although there remains much uncertainty about the wider economy and the country's recovery from the Coronavirus pandemic, the outlook for graduate recruitment at the start of the 2021-2022 academic year seems considerably brighter than it did 18 months ago.

Together, the graduate employers listed in *The Times Top 100 Graduate Employers* are predicting that they will have 24,378 graduate vacancies for autumn 2022 start dates. This is 5.5 per cent more than the number of university-leavers recruited in 2021 and – combined with the increase in recruitment in 2021 – it restores more than three-quarters of the graduate vacancies that were lost in 2020.

Almost half of the UK's top employers are planning to hire more graduates in 2022. A third think they will match their previous intake, but a sixth of organisations are likely to recruit fewer university-leavers over the next 12 months.

Graduate recruitment is expected to rise in thirteen out of fifteen key industries and business sectors in the year ahead, with the largest number of additional vacancies available at the leading banking & finance employers, the top accounting & professional services firms, media organisations, public sector employers and technology companies.

Employers in the investment banking and legal sectors remain the most consistent graduate recruiters, having made no cuts to their recruitment in 2020 before maintaining graduate vacancies in 2021 and 2022 at levels that match the sectors' pre-pandemic recruitment.

The largest number of graduate vacancies in 2022 is expected to be at the accounting & professional firms and amongst the public sector employers, with a total of more than 10,000 entry-level positions available for new graduates. In all, fifteen of the eighteen top employers in these sectors are preparing to recruit additional graduates in the coming year.

For the fourth consecutive year, the organisation with the biggest graduate recruitment target within *The Times Top 100 Graduate Employers* is Teach First. The popular programme that recruits new graduates to teach in schools in low-income

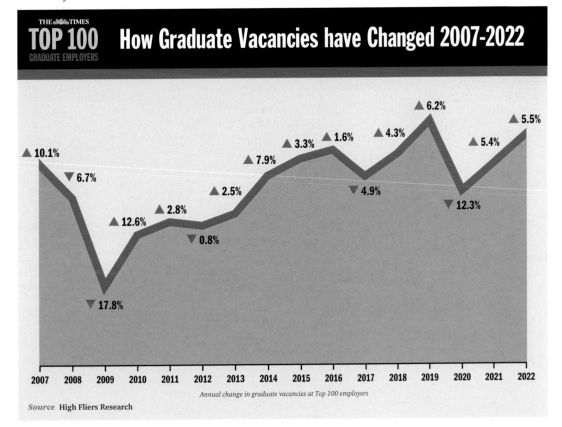

THE TIMES TOP 100 GRADUATE EMPLOYERS

How Graduate Vacancies have Changed 2007-2022

▲ 10.1%
▼ 6.7%
▲ 12.6%
▲ 2.8%
▼ 0.8%
▲ 2.5%
▲ 7.9%
▲ 3.3%
▲ 1.6%
▼ 4.9%
▲ 4.3%
▲ 6.2%
▼ 12.3%
▲ 5.4%
▲ 5.5%
▼ 17.8%

2007 2008 2009 2010 2011 2012 2013 2014 2015 2016 2017 2018 2019 2020 2021 2022

Annual change in graduate vacancies at Top 100 employers

Source High Fliers Research

communities around the UK has 1,750 places available in 2022.

Other very substantial individual graduate recruiters include the accounting & professional services firms – PwC (1,200 graduate vacancies), Deloitte and KPMG (1,000 vacancies) and EY (950 vacancies) – the Civil Service Fast Stream (950 vacancies), online retailer Amazon (800 vacancies) and Enterprise (800 vacancies).

Two-thirds of graduate employers featured in this year's *Top 100* are offering between 50 and 250 vacancies for 2022, a quarter have fewer than 50 positions available, and three organisations aren't planning to recruit any graduates this year.

Three-fifths of employers have vacancies for graduates in technology, over half have opportunities in finance, and more than a third are recruiting for general management vacancies, human resources roles, engineering positions or sales and marketing jobs.

A fifth of the country's top graduate employers are looking for new recruits to work in research & development, but there are fewer graduate jobs available in retailing or in more specialist areas, such as logistics & supply chain, purchasing, property and the media.

More than four-fifths of *Top 100* employers have graduate vacancies in London in 2021, and

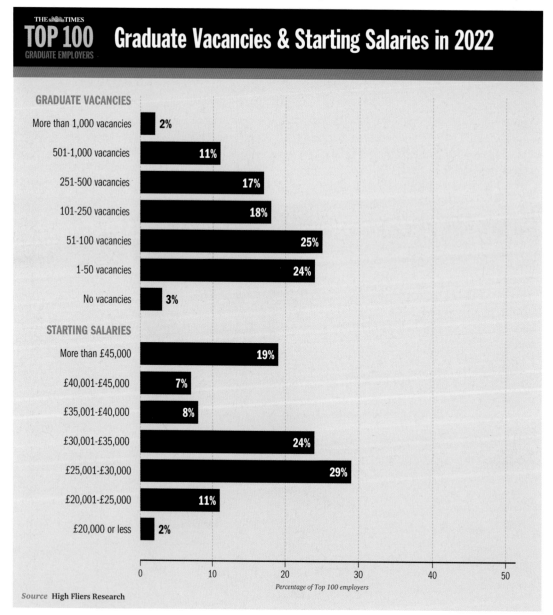

THE TIMES **TOP 100** GRADUATE EMPLOYERS **Graduate Vacancies & Starting Salaries in 2022**

GRADUATE VACANCIES

More than 1,000 vacancies	2%
501-1,000 vacancies	11%
251-500 vacancies	17%
101-250 vacancies	18%
51-100 vacancies	25%
1-50 vacancies	24%
No vacancies	3%

STARTING SALARIES

More than £45,000	19%
£40,001-£45,000	7%
£35,001-£40,000	8%
£30,001-£35,000	24%
£25,001-£30,000	29%
£20,001-£25,000	11%
£20,000 or less	2%

Percentage of Top 100 employers

Source **High Fliers Research**

Our door is open.
And so are our minds.

With strong career pathways, unlimited learning and a real drive toward true diversity and inclusion, you can be proud to work for us.

BT.com/graduates

half have posts available elsewhere in the south east of England. Up to half also have roles in the north west of England, the south west, the Midlands, Yorkshire and the north east. Over two-fifths are recruiting for graduate roles in Scotland, but Northern Ireland, Wales and East Anglia have the fewest employers with vacancies this year.

Graduate starting salaries at the UK's leading employers have changed little over the last decade and are unlikely to rise in the coming year. After annual increases every year up to 2010, the average salary on offer from the country's top employers remained at £29,000 for four consecutive years, before increasing again in 2014 and 2015.

The average graduate starting salary in 2021 was £30,000, unchanged for the seventh year running. The highest starting salaries for the 'Class of 2022' are expected to be at the leading investment banks and fund managers (a median of £50,000), consulting firms (£47,000) and law firms (£45,000).

More than a quarter of employers featured in *The Times Top 100 Graduate Employers* are now offering starting salaries of at least £40,000 for their new recruits. The most generous graduate salaries publicised within this edition are at the leading law firms Linklaters, White & Case and Latham & Watkins, which are each paying new trainees starting salaries of £50,000 in 2022.

Consulting firm Newton and technology company TPP also offer graduate packages of up to £50,000, whilst a further six legal firms have starting salaries of between £45,000 and £48,000. Retailer Aldi continues to pay a sector-leading graduate starting salary of £44,000, plus a fully expensed company car.

More than a third of the UK's leading employers now recruit graduates year-round, or in different phases during the year, and will accept applications throughout the 2021-2022 recruitment season until all their vacancies are filled. For employers with an annual application deadline, most are in November or December, although a limited number have October or post-Christmas deadlines for their graduate programmes.

Up to half of this year's *Top 100* employers require that applicants for their graduate schemes should have a 2.1 degree or better, and a quarter specify a minimum UCAS tariff too – mostly in the range of 'ABB' to 'BCC' grades at A-level.

Whilst the graduate job market will undoubtedly remain highly competitive in 2022, it is encouraging that – for the second year running – the organisations featured in *The Times Top 100 Graduate Employers* will be offering more entry-level vacancies for university-leavers and a wide range of opportunities in different industries and business sectors.

THE TIMES TOP 100 GRADUATE EMPLOYERS — Graduate Vacancies at Top 100 Employers in 2022

	2021		GRADUATE VACANCIES IN 2022	% CHANGE IN 2022	% CHANGE IN 2021	MEDIAN STARTING SALARY IN 2022
1.	2	ACCOUNTANCY & PROFESSIONAL SERVICES FIRMS	5,800	▲ 3.8%	▲ 3.7%	£30,600
2.	1	PUBLIC SECTOR EMPLOYERS	4,690	▲ 4.1%	▼ 6.7%	£23,100
3.	3	TECHNOLOGY COMPANIES	2,355	▲ 5.4%	▲ 19.8%	£32,000
4.	4	INVESTMENT BANKS & FUND MANAGERS	1,980	▲ 1.8%	▼ 2.0%	£50,000
5.	7	ENGINEERING & INDUSTRIAL COMPANIES	1,925	▼ 5.4%	▲ 36.0%	£28,000
6.	5	BANKING & FINANCIAL SERVICES	1,525	▲ 16.8%	▼ 20.2%	£40,000
7.	10	RETAILERS	1,310	▲ 49.2%	▲ 57.6%	£36,800
8.	6	ARMED FORCES	1,100	▲ 1.9%	▲ 0.6%	£33,000
9.	8	LAW FIRMS	866	▲ 5.9%	▲ 0.6%	£47,000
10.	9	MEDIA ORGANISATIONS	855	▲ 29.2%	▲ 8.8%	£31,500
11.	12	CONSULTING FIRMS	380	▲ 22.2%	▲ 36.4%	£45,000
12.	11	CONSUMER GOODS MANUFACTURERS	270	▲ 17.4%	▼ 16.7%	£32,000
13.	14	CHEMICAL & PHARMACEUTICAL COMPANIES	190	▲ 6.7%	▼ 2.5%	£30,600
14.	13	OIL & ENERGY COMPANIES	140	▲ 33.3%	▼ 37.1%	£35,000
15.	14	CHARITIES & VOLUNTARY SECTOR	112	▼ 1.8%	▲ 34.1%	£20,200

Source High Fliers Research

THG

Push *limits.*
Break *boundaries.*
Make an *impact.*

Choose a career *less* ordinary.

Find out more about our
exciting career paths at
THG.com/careers

**Graduate Management
Training Scheme**

65 years of making a difference

If you want to come to work every day knowing what you're doing really matters, our scheme is for you

The NHS Graduate Management Training Scheme has been changing the lives of graduates and patients for 6 decades. For 65 hugely successful years the Scheme has been responsible for the recruitment of thousands of future senior leaders who every day make a difference and have a positive impact on people's lives.

The NHS has a workforce of over 1.3m people all with the same ambition to improve patient care. Even though the Scheme is not offering clinical roles it is clear that non-clinical roles across our NHS can influence and make a huge positive change to our National Health Service and its service users.

If you are somebody who wants to come to work every day knowing what you are doing really matters, the NHS and our Scheme is for you.

We have a proud history, come and be part of the future.

 NHSGraduateScheme   nhsgraduatescheme

 @NHSGradScheme   NHS Graduate Management
Training Scheme

Visit: www.nhsgraduates.co.uk

Graduate Job Hunting in the Pandemic

By **Marc Lintern**
President of the Association of Graduate Careers Advisory Services
Director of Careers Service & Deputy Academic Registrar, Newcastle University

Over the last year, almost every aspect of graduate recruitment has changed – from the way employers promote their vacancies at universities to the selection processes used to assess which candidates are awarded graduate job offers.

Despite this, careers services at universities across the UK have continued to provide ongoing support to their students and graduates throughout the pandemic. And while the employment situation has been very challenging, labour market specialists claim that the graduate job market has not been hit so hard as other parts of the economy.

Reflecting on the past year, for graduates who left university in the summer of 2021, the Coronavirus pandemic meant that their final year of studies was dominated by lockdowns, self-isolating, online learning, and limited or non-existent social lives. However, by successfully navigating this difficult period, graduates have at the same time demonstrated resilience, adaptability, perseverance and a positive outlook – all attributes that employers are seeking.

While none of the country's well-known employers were able to run their usual on-campus graduate recruitment campaigns during 2020-2021, university careers services helped employers move their presentations, workshops and other recruitment activities online. And although autumn careers fairs had to be cancelled, these were turned into virtual events or replaced with additional employer presentations.

From the spring of 2020 onwards, university careers services also switched their own support, advice and careers guidance online too. With most staff working from home, careers teams quickly adapted to provide all of their normal services to students remotely.

This included individual one-to-one careers guidance, which moved from inside careers services to Zoom, Teams or telephone consultations and – with this shift supported by email advice – it enabled university careers services to offer a record level of support to student job hunters during the year.

Adapting to these changes, some careers services introduced special workshops on how to get the most out of employers' online events and activities, as well as on how to network successfully or connect with employers remotely. Others focused on preparing for virtual interviews and employers' new online assessment centres.

Although employers weren't able to visit universities in person during the past year, most have delivered their presentations online – either as major national live-streamed events or university-specific presentations. Without

The graduate job market is looking more optimistic but many of the most sought-after vacancies are likely to be filled very quickly.

YOU
ARE THE
FUTURE
OF BARCLAYS

Bring us your energy and curiosity.
Bring us new ideas, agility and
adaptability. Show us your potential
and your will to succeed. And we'll give
you a wealth of experience, knowledge,
support – and real-world challenge on
projects that really matter. We'll give
you the inspiring future you aspire to.

**To find out more, type
search.jobs.barclays**

having to physically travel round the country for these events, many employers were actually able to reach a wider audience of students at more universities than they had done pre-pandemic – although many job hunters will inevitably have missed out on opportunities for informal chats and discussions with recruiters and recent graduates visiting their campus. And because presentations and workshops hosted by university careers services and employers were often recorded for students to watch in their own time, it has helped make these events more accessible.

Because of the pandemic, final year students from the 'Class of 2021' had fewer opportunities to build up their CVs, develop their employability skills and 'add value' to their degrees through work experience or volunteering. The majority of national internships and work experience programmes in the summer of 2020 were moved to shorter virtual experiences or cancelled altogether, although many careers services have countered this by offering more internship programmes with local small and medium-sized businesses.

Of course, another challenge for students, graduates and careers services, has been the seemingly constant messages in the media about how hard the job market was being hit by the lockdowns – and the millions of people on furlough. This left many of last year's finalists thinking they wouldn't get a job after university,

---

THE TIMES TOP 100 GRADUATE EMPLOYERS — How the Pandemic affected the 'Class of 2021'

UNIVERSITY CAREERS SERVICES

A record **71%** of students used their **university careers services website**

1 in **6** finalists had **one-to-one consultations** with careers advisers online or by phone

EMPLOYER PRESENTATIONS & CAREERS FAIRS

More than a **quarter** of final year students took part in **virtual careers fairs**

A **third** of finalists watched or participated in **employers' online presentations**

WORK EXPERIENCE

Almost **half** of students' planned **internships** were cancelled in summer 2020

A **third** of students did their work experience as **virtual internships**

JOB HUNTING

1 in **3** finalists thought they'd have to take **'any job they were offered'** in 2021

A **sixth** stopped graduate job hunting because of their **mental health**

JOB APPLICATIONS

Final year students made an average of **13 applications** each, **a third more** than the previous highest average

GRADUATE JOB OFFERS

A **third** fewer finalists received a **graduate job offer** before leaving university, compared with 2020

Source **High Fliers Research** 16,121 final year students leaving UK universities in the summer of 2021 were asked about the impact of the Coronavirus pandemic on their careers research and graduate job hunting, during interviews for *The UK Graduate Careers Survey 2021*

CHARACTER IS EVERYTHING

From Arthur Guinness to Johnnie Walker, our business was founded on people of character. Our graduates are making sure we bring that character with us and remain the world's leading premium alcohol company. It's their determination that makes our iconic brands even stronger. Its why we trust them with our legacy. And its why we reward them with the career-defining opportunities.

Find out more and apply.

Diageo.com/Careers

DIAGEO

and inevitably affected their confidence in the employment market and in themselves. And with the collapse of much of the hospitality industry and large parts of the retail sector, there were also fewer temporary jobs available for new graduates while searching for their ideal opportunity.

In terms of graduate roles, three-quarters of university careers services reported a fall in the number of graduate jobs being advertised during 2020-2021, but the majority of the UK's best-known employers did continue with their recruitment, albeit with reduced numbers or delayed start dates.

With this combination of uncertainty over the graduate job market, anxiety over career prospects, reduced confidence about personal worth, and the impact of Coronavirus on student life, one of the most worrying impacts has been on the number of students who have delayed – or opted out of – graduate job hunting. While this may be a normal response, there are graduate roles available, and while it may take time to get the job that you want, you should speak to your careers service about the support and advice you need to achieve this.

But what is the outlook for today's students who will be graduating in 2022 or beyond?

If the past year was characterised at most universities as a 'digital first' approach – for academic courses, careers guidance and graduate recruitment – then 2021-2022 is set to be a year of 'blended' provision. The majority of university careers services are expecting to reopen on campus and will be offering students a choice of face-to-face and online activities, guidance and support during the year.

It isn't clear whether employers will be able to return for in-person recruitment presentations and skills workshops in the autumn – although many are keen to, as soon as it is safe – but most will be offering a programme of national and local events online. And while it's unlikely that on-campus careers fairs will be able to run just yet, because of the difficulties of hosting mass events while the pandemic continues, many universities are hopeful that they could return in the spring.

For students graduating in the summer of 2022, it's important to start job hunting as soon as you can, get in early with your applications and be persistent. The graduate job market is looking more optimistic but, as is the case every year, many of the most sought-after vacancies are likely to be filled very quickly.

THE TIMES TOP 100 GRADUATE EMPLOYERS — Graduates' Plans for After University in 2021

- NO DEFINITE PLANS — 12%
- TAKING TIME OFF OR GOING TRAVELLING — 10%
- EXPECTING TO START A GRADUATE JOB — 22%
- EXPECTING TO BE LOOKING FOR A GRADUATE JOB — 17%
- EXPECTING TO DO VOLUNTARY OR TEMPORARY WORK — 5%
- PLANNING TO RUN OWN BUSINESS — 2%
- INTENDING TO DO A POSTGRADUATE COURSE — 32%

Source **High Fliers Research** 16,121 final year students leaving UK universities in the summer of 2021 were asked about their plans for after university, during interviews for *The UK Graduate Careers Survey 2021*

Don't just rely on the First or 2.1 degree you're hoping to achieve to land you your first graduate job. As things open up further, try to get work experience of any kind, make the most of extracurricular activities through university clubs and societies, and get involved with your community and with volunteering. With fewer formal internships available, employers have had to think about students' skills in a new way and will value all of these experiences.

The pandemic has made many people rethink what they want to do in the future, so now – more than ever before – you should aim for things that are going to make you happy and apply for jobs that you really want to do. You may not find your ideal job straight after university, but as long as it's a step towards what you want to do, that's a positive thing.

It may be better to take a job that isn't in the direction you want to take eventually, simply to get valuable experience in the workplace. It's always easier to apply for another job once you have one – and being employed will help build your skills, knowledge, confidence and professional networks.

Of course, university careers services don't just advise students about applying for jobs. Many students are interested in running their own business or applying for a postgraduate course.

In terms of starting a business, careers services either have their own 'start-up' teams, to help you get your business off the ground, or they will be able to refer you to other departments in your university that can help you. This may be a far more viable option than you think, so if you have a business idea or you simply know that you want to work for yourself or create your own job, careers services can help.

Regarding postgraduate study: record numbers of students who graduated in 2020 and 2021 opted to do a further course, and so the first question to expect from a careers adviser will often be around your motive. This is because – although there are plenty of positive reasons for doing further study – careers advisers worry about graduates who use postgraduate study simply as a way of deferring their decision-making about what to do next, or because they couldn't get the graduate job they want.

Although doing a 'panic Masters' may seem like a good back-up plan, it does come at a price – not just in terms of more tuition fees but also the additional living expenses of an extra year or two at university. Careers advisers will always urge those considering postgraduate study to do it for the right reason. That could be because you need vocational or professional training for careers such as law, teaching or journalism. Or it might be to gain a competitive advantage with a higher qualification in science, engineering or management.

Equally, choosing a course because you simply want to spend longer studying a subject you've loved as an undergraduate can be a very good motive. If you're not sure, contact your university careers service, and they will help you work through the pros and cons, offering impartial advice to help you make a decision.

And this, of course, is the case whatever path you're considering for life after graduation. Make the most of your university careers service and the wealth of information, knowledge, support and experience it can offer. Careers services are entirely impartial and want what's right for you as an individual – they're not there to sell you any particular career, employment opportunity or path after university.

While the last 18 months have been very challenging, one of the benefits the pandemic has brought is the fact that university careers services are now far more accessible to recent graduates who are still looking for work. Graduates can access one-to-one guidance and join online workshops and employers' virtual presentations from wherever they are – it no longer matters if they aren't on campus. Graduates can also hear first-hand about immediate vacancies or employers with different start dates during the year.

Many careers services ask graduates to register for ongoing support, so they know who to help – so just get in touch with your careers service and ask what they recommend. Most universities provide ongoing support and, while some specialise in early career progression – for up to three years after graduates have completed their degrees – others offer lifelong support.

The most crucial thing if you're looking to start your first graduate job in 2022 is not to panic, and not to think that there aren't opportunities for you. The labour market and the wider economy are improving rapidly as the country recovers from the devastating effects of the pandemic, and the prospects for new graduates are improving too. But it may take time, effort and resilience to find the job you want for after university.

Build your own career

With an exciting range of career options, great rewards and benefits, good opportunities to progress and full support at every step, RSM is the perfect place to build your career.

Experience the power of being understood.

Experience RSM | **rsmuk.com**

THE POWER OF BEING UNDERSTOOD
AUDIT | TAX | CONSULTING

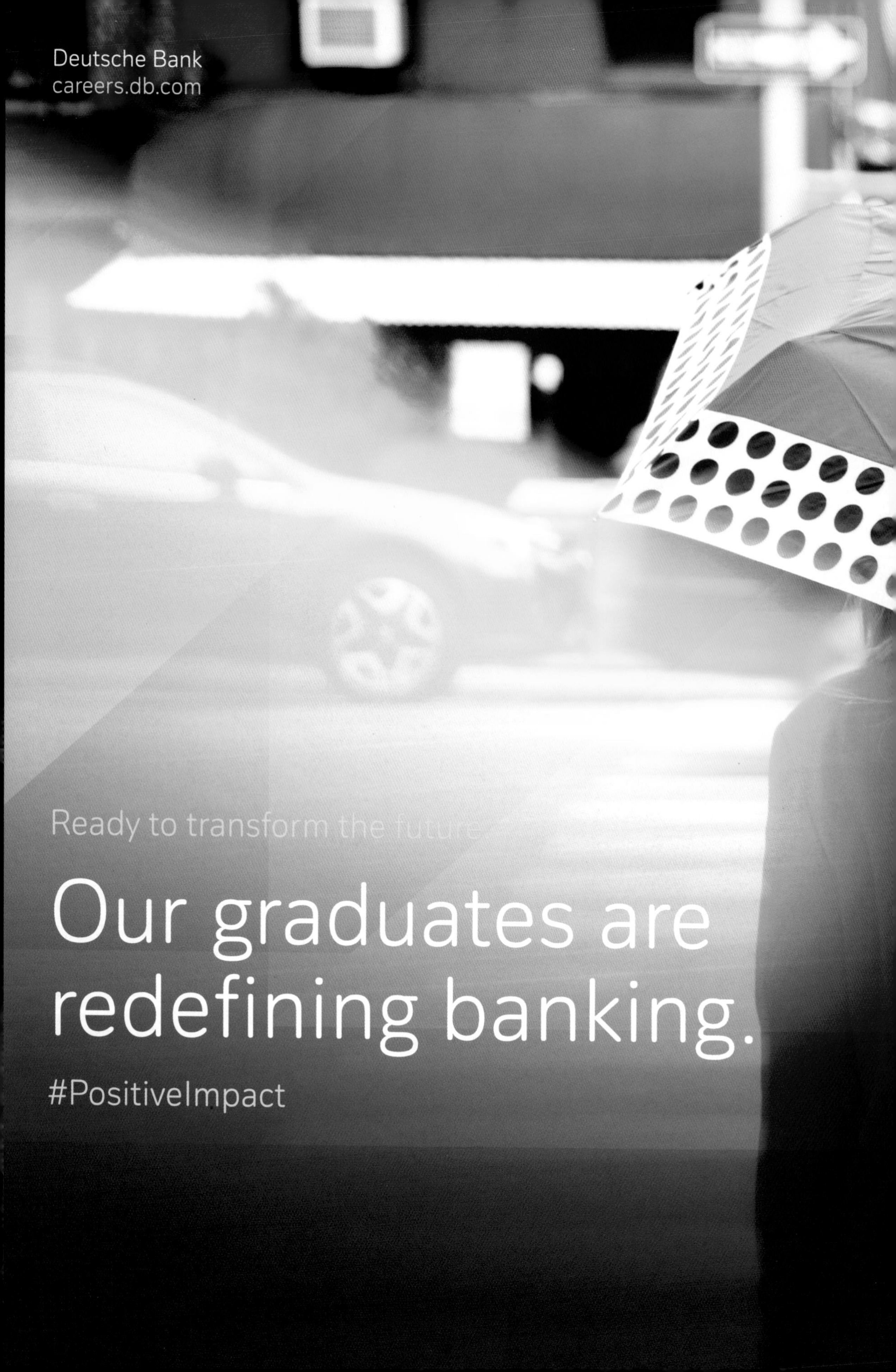

Deutsche Bank
careers.db.com

Ready to transform the future

Our graduates are redefining banking.

#PositiveImpact

At Deutsche Bank, we're changing what it means to be a bank.

By bringing together people, technology and innovation, we are making a positive difference for our colleagues, our clients and society.

We know that genuine innovation and progress comes from creative thinking and diverse perspectives. You'll see first-hand how our supportive and inclusive culture encourages our people to innovate and build products and services that push the boundaries of what's possible in finance.

Here, your ideas will always have impact. From your first day, you'll experience the learning, support and exposure you need to build a career defined by the impact you make.

If you have the creativity and curiosity to build the bank of tomorrow, this is where you belong.

Unlock your potential and make an impact.
Visit www.careers.db.com

Student Opportunities with #TeamAmex

AMERICAN EXPRES

Discover a career as unique as you.

With meaningful mentorships, real-world responsibilities, and hands-on learning experiences, your time on #TeamAmex can shape your career journey for years to come. And, as an equal opportunity employer, you can build a global network with colleagues from many diverse backgrounds, lifestyles and locations. Join us and let's lead the way together.

Britain's Graduate Employers and the Coronavirus Pandemic

Interviews by **Martin Birchall**

THE TIMES
TOP 100
GRADUATE EMPLOYERS

How the country's leading graduate employers have risen to the challenges of the Coronavirus pandemic.

PHARMACEUTICALS

Producing a Coronavirus vaccine for the world

Its vaccine success has made AstraZeneca one of the UK's best-known companies and is inspiring a new generation of university-leavers to pursue careers in science.

Before the onset of the Coronavirus pandemic, few outside of the pharmaceuticals industry knew of the Anglo-Swedish company AstraZeneca which has its global headquarters in Cambridge.

But its pioneering partnership with scientists from the University of Oxford to produce a successful COVID-19 vaccine has turned the company into a household name worldwide.

"It's been a whirlwind year from a recruitment perspective," says Adam Isle, AstraZeneca's global acquisition lead for early talent. "Having such a high profile during the pandemic has encouraged more students to explore our exciting career opportunities, not just in research & development, but also in operations, technology, and across the business."

Adam Isle, Global Aquisition Lead for Early Talent, AstraZeneca

Across its graduate programmes, applications have jumped by 135% in 2021 – a significant increase on the already healthy levels of interest in some of the company's most important entry-level schemes.

"We're a very science-driven organisation," explains Isle. "And we're looking for graduates who are excited by cutting-edge research and who understand the value of the work we do for patients worldwide, whatever their field of study."

A number of AstraZeneca's graduates worked directly on the company's pandemic response. "It was certainly a once-in-a-lifetime opportunity," says Isle. "Some of our R&D graduates did important work at the Coronavirus testing laboratory in Cambridge. And graduates working in operations have helped maintain the supply chain for the vaccine, which was key to the success of AstraZeneca's efforts globally."

Prior to the pandemic, AstraZeneca was best known for its treatments

and drugs for cancer, cardiovascular, renal and metabolic diseases, and immunology and respiratory conditions such as asthma and chronic pulmonary disease.

"The company has had considerable success over the last four or five years and has developed a strong pipeline of new drugs in different treatment areas," explains Isle. "We're an entrepreneurial organisation and follow the science. This fosters a dynamic, energising culture that has helped us to respond very quickly during the pandemic."

This success means the company has been expanding its recruitment and is expecting to recruit over 90 graduates for its global development programmes in 2022. "It can take ten years or longer to develop new drugs or treatments and bring them to patients globally, so we make long-term investments in our talent pipeline, and recruit graduates and other early talent across our organisation," Isle says.

"Many of our opportunities are in R&D or pharmaceutical technology & development, but our operations

and technology leadership graduate programmes are equally important," he continues.

"Our biometrics and data sciences & artificial intelligence programmes are also very popular and help us deliver cutting-edge science. And because our work during the pandemic has transformed our profile, more graduates from computer science and programming backgrounds – who might previously have only considered applying to the well-known brands in the tech sector – are discovering that AstraZeneca is a real technology innovator too and offers careers where you can make an impact on patients' lives."

Isle and AstraZeneca's early talent teams are hoping to be back out on campus during 2021-2022. "We're always looking to increase the diversity of applications for our graduate programmes," he says. "And we want to turn students and graduates on to the opportunities at AstraZeneca, in biopharmaceuticals and across the UK's vibrant life sciences industry, whatever their background."

Helena Sharpe, Head of EMEA Campus Recruiting, J.P. Morgan

INVESTMENT BANKING

Business as usual in the City

The UK economy is still reeling from the effects of the pandemic, but the top investment banks are thriving.

The Coronavirus crisis plunged the country into its deepest recession for three hundred years, and yet several of the leading investment banks have had one of their most successful and profitable periods of the last two decades.

"We have maintained our hiring throughout the pandemic, bringing in a similar number of graduates in both 2020 and 2021 as we did in 2019," says Helena Sharpe, executive director and head of campus recruiting for Europe, the Middle East and Africa at J.P. Morgan. "And despite all the doom and gloom you see in the news, there's so much growth in key parts of the bank that we think there'll be even more interns and graduates needed next year – and we're actually adding extra recruiters to our team in preparation for this."

A large proportion of J.P. Morgan's graduates are recruited through summer internships for students at the end of their penultimate year at university. "We ran our internships in the summer of 2020 virtually and they were reduced down to five weeks," explains Sharpe. "But students were paid in full for the ten weeks' experience that they'd been expecting – and we made a similar number of graduate jobs offers as usual at the end of the summer."

Putting the internships online meant that J.P. Morgan could deliver the experience simultaneously to all of its students worldwide. "For example, our investment banking interns had live case studies that they worked on as a group, both locally and globally, which gave everyone the same consistent experience," Sharpe says. "It was hard to show what it would be like working day-to-day in a particular team, but we used real-life examples, and interns worked directly with the managers that graduates report to when they join the bank."

Internships in the summer of 2021 were a mix of in-person and virtual experiences. "Our students mirrored what was going on in the business," explains Sharpe. "So our markets and investment banking interns were based in the office, whereas our technology and corporate functions were working from home."

J.P. Morgan is keen for its internships to return to its Canary Wharf headquarters in 2022, providing restrictions allow it. "There are some elements that don't translate into a virtual format," Sharpe admits. "We used to have big social events for our interns during the summer, as well as a community day and a 5k run in Battersea Park. Online quizzes aren't quite the same as connecting with people in person."

The pandemic has also changed the way J.P. Morgan promotes its graduate opportunities to university students. "The annual campus recruiting cycle has always been quite traditional and one of the things we were trying to do, even before Coronavirus, was to move away from having strict lists of target universities and to open up our applications to more people," says Sharpe.

"Switching to virtual events over the last eighteen months has helped level the playing field a little and makes us more accessible to everyone," she continues. "We want all students to feel that they have a chance to do well here – and that you didn't have to go to certain university to get in."

J.P. Morgan is also being more flexible about how and when new graduates join the bank. "Historically our main graduate start dates have been in August or September, but our technology and wealth management programmes now have January intakes as well," says Sharpe. "And in some business areas we're offering off-cycle internships for new graduates too, so that they can do three months after they've graduated and then go straight into graduate roles."

Sharpe is upbeat about the prospects for next year's university-leavers. "We're reporting good business results and recruiting more graduates than ever," she reflects. "So I think people can feel secure about accepting a job offer here."

ENGINEERING & INDUSTRIAL

Engineering for the long-term

With new products that can take decades to design, develop and deliver, BAE Systems couldn't let the pandemic disrupt its graduate recruitment.

Fabien Littel, Head of UK Graduate Programmes, BAE Systems

In the summer of 2020, just as several of the best-known employers from the engineering & industrial sector were taking the difficult decision to scale back or pause their graduate recruitment because of the Coronavirus crisis, the multinational defence and aerospace company BAE Systems was preparing for one of its biggest ever intakes of new graduates.

"We were in a very fortunate position because of the type of products and services that BAE Systems produces," explains Fabien Littel, the company's head of UK graduate programmes. "Our long-term contracts to deliver things like new nuclear submarines and the next-generation fighter jets and naval ships meant that this work had to continue uninterrupted, in order to deliver to our customers. Today's graduates will play a vital role in these projects in the future, so the demand for new talent didn't change because of the pandemic."

It can take 20 years or more to develop these types of products –

from initial design to final delivery to BAE Systems' customers. "The high-calibre graduates we recruit bring energy, fresh thinking and passion to the work we do and are such an important part of our organisational culture," Littel says. "We look for a good mix of graduates with different aspirations, whether that's to become one of our managing directors or a specialist product developer."

BAE Systems has recently moved to three start dates each year for its graduate programmes, in the autumn, winter and early summer. "Almost all of our new graduates were able to join as planned in September 2020, but some moved to the January intake instead," explains Littel.

"Many of the office-based graduates worked from home, but our on-site teams did a great deal to make sure those working in a manufacturing environment could do so safely," he continues. "And all of our new graduates took part in an extensive two-week induction to prepare them for their roles and to help them understand the wider

organisation and the way they would be working."

The pandemic has changed the way BAE Systems delivers some of the training for its new graduates. "As part of their development programme, each of our graduates receives ten days' training on core skills and personal effectiveness skills, as well as one-to-one coaching," says Littel. "By doing it online, we can bring together colleagues working on submarines in Barrow in the north west of England with those designing naval ships in Portsmouth and our teams in Farnborough or Glasgow. It's a great way to develop graduates' awareness of what BAE Systems does as a whole and to grow their individual networks."

The company has recruited over 350 graduates in 2021 – along with around 200 undergraduates for its 12-week summer internships and 12-month industrial placements – and is expecting that its 2022 intake could be bigger still.

"Just over half of our graduate vacancies are in engineering roles but we have opportunities in every part of the business, from project management and procurement to information management & technology and human resources," Littel says. "Our new graduate programme means that graduates go straight into their chosen role, rather than the series of rotations that we offered previously, so that enables graduates to make a real contribution within weeks of joining."

"We'll be taking a hybrid approach to our recruitment promotions during 2021-2022. By taking part in virtual careers fairs and online presentations, we've been able to reach wider and more diverse audiences than ever before over the last year," he continues. "But we're also keen to return to university campuses for targeted events that will help us reach the students and graduates who are most likely to be interested in joining BAE Systems after completing their studies."

Broadcasting to the nation in times of crisis

From journalists to broadcast engineers, the BBC's new graduates and apprentices rose to the challenge of keeping the corporation on-air during the pandemic.

Rob Alcock, Head of the BBC Academy

On Monday 23rd March 2020, 15 million people switched on BBC One to hear Prime Minister Boris Johnson's broadcast from 10 Downing Street, solemnly intoning that the nation must stay at home to beat Coronavirus.

In the week that followed, 82% of all adults in the UK turned to BBC News for updates on the crisis, and usage of the BBC's iPlayer service jumped by more than 60% during the spring, as the country entertained itself with streaming and box sets during the lockdown.

At the start of the pandemic, the BBC had around 290 graduates, apprentices and trainees working in different parts of the organisation. "It was a really difficult time, but we put in place everything we could to enable them to continue working and keep learning and developing," says Rob Alcock, head of the BBC Academy which runs the corporation's graduate and apprenticeship schemes.

"We only had people in offices who were 'broadcast-critical', so many of our new recruits who were working in broadcast and technology roles found themselves at the sharp end of our operations," he explains. "There was an awful lot of radio and TV production that was happening from people's homes, and our graduates and apprentices played a key role in getting this content on air, working in control rooms or studios on their own, under the experienced eye of someone who was working remotely. It was incredibly challenging but a fantastic opportunity too."

Trainee journalists often found themselves filming stories on their phones, before editing them themselves. "A lot of the pictures you see on the news are shot on iPhones now, which has been invaluable during the pandemic," Alcock says. "By using this kind of technology, they were able to make a real contribution from wherever they were working."

The BBC's new recruits continued with their training and development throughout the different lockdowns. "We worked with our training providers to bring forward knowledge training for our graduates and apprentices, to help keep them fully occupied in the periods they weren't able to do more of the practical parts of their training," explains Alcock.

"By the time the pandemic struck, the BBC Academy had already moved most of its learning resources into the online environment, so we provided additional virtual training to ensure our graduates and apprentices were using every opportunity to learn."

Not all of the BBC's planned recruitment could continue during the pandemic. "The BBC has traditionally followed the annual academic cycle for its recruitment," Alcock says. "But over the last 18 months we did defer some of our corporate and technology schemes, and paused recruitment for production and journalism. This means that this year's cycle has been pushed back slightly, but we expect it to return to the traditional timetable in 2022."

One thing that hasn't changed since the start of the Coronavirus pandemic is graduates' enthusiasm for working at the BBC. Each year it receives tens of thousands of applications from university-leavers for its entry-level training schemes.

"We've always been vastly oversubscribed, which is a great compliment to us and means we have a vast range of talent to choose from," reflects Alcock. "The BBC stands and falls on its creativity, so we're looking for people from all backgrounds and walks of life that are representative of our audience, who can bring that creativity and their fresh ideas to the heart of the organisation," he continues. "And we've got big ambitions to expand our entry-level recruitment over the next four to five years."

"Although it's an office job, it just doesn't feel like an office. Everyone is so friendly and relaxed. And I love putting my coding skills into practice"

Admiral

Putting wellbeing at the heart of recruitment

In a year like no other for university students and graduates starting their first job, the 'Big Four' professional services firm EY has focused on mental health and wellbeing.

By the time the Coronavirus pandemic took hold of the UK in March 2020, many of the country's top employers had already made job offers to the 'Class of 2020' for their autumn intake of graduates. But it would be weeks, and in some cases months, before final year students found out whether they'd be able to join their new employer.

"We were really pleased that we were able to take on all of the graduates we'd planned to, because it was obviously such an uncertain time for so many people," says Victoria Alcock, senior talent attraction and acquisition manager at EY, one of the 'Big Four' accounting & professional services firms.

Victoria Alcock, Senior Talent Attraction & Acquisition Manager, EY

Over 800 graduates joined EY in the autumn of 2020, but many found themselves working remotely, rather than starting their training at the firms' offices around the UK.

"We've been very conscious that many of our new graduates were having to work alone from home instead of being surrounded by a team, which can be really tough and very lonely for them," explains Alcock. "They haven't been able to meet as a graduate cohort, as they would do in normal times, but the firm has put a great deal of support in place and our trainees have been able to spend some time in the office and go out to clients, when the restrictions have allowed it."

Mental health and wellbeing also played a key part in EY's recruitment campaign during 2020-2021. "We moved all our usual campus promotions online and took part in a lot of virtual events and activities during the autumn," says Alcock. "But then in February, we launched our 'EY & You' wellbeing week."

The firm brought together celebrities and experts – including

Dr Alex George from ITV's *Love Island*, boxer Anthony Joshua and Michelle Visage – with EY panellists who shared their perspectives on topics such as mental health, motivation, positivity, confidence and mindfulness. "We really wanted to support students who'd been struggling with the lockdowns and university life during the pandemic," she explains.

Applications for graduate jobs in the accounting & professional services sector reached a five-year high in 2021, with more university-leavers keen to get a recognised qualification and join employers that offer better job security for the future. "The pandemic has brought a great deal of change," Alcock says. "But companies still need to be audited and people still need to do their tax returns, so there continues to be a strong demand for graduates at EY."

EY is expecting to recruit a bumper intake of new graduates in 2022. "We're in a great position as a business and are looking to increase our graduate recruitment, particularly in areas like technology

and consulting," explains Alcock. "Around half of these roles will be outside London and we've built on our long-standing culture of flexible working, so graduates will divide their time between working in the office, on clients' sites and at home."

The firm is hoping it may be able to return to doing some campus promotions in the year ahead, but will be continuing with its programme of online events and publicity.

"The pandemic has shown us that by running our virtual events as a centralised programme and advertising them to as many different universities as we can, we've managed to reach more students than ever before," Alcock enthuses.

"This approach means we've been able to introduce EY to people who hadn't heard of us previously or who weren't considering a career in our sector, which is really exciting as diversity is such an important focus for us. And we're very proud that it has helped us climb to number six in this year's edition of *The Times Top 100 Graduate Employers*, which is the firm's best ever ranking."

Camilla Sanger, Recruitment Partner, Slaughter and May

LAW

The challenges of working from home in the legal sector

Like many other graduate employers, the City's top law firms swapped their long hours in the office for a new regime of working from home during the pandemic.

Graduates who joined law firm Slaughter and May in March 2020 began their training just days before the first national lockdown.

"Those new trainees had very little time in the office before we had to send them home," remembers Camilla Sanger, recruitment partner at Slaughter and May. "It's been a real challenge for us to make sure that all the trainees who've started work with us since that first lockdown have had the same learning and development as if they'd been in the office. When you're a trainee, it's so important to learn by osmosis, by being in the same room as your supervisor."

The firm put in place additional training, mentoring and wellbeing sessions for its trainees, along with departmental events and social initiatives online, to help them integrate into the firm, albeit remotely. "A great deal of thought went into how we could replicate the experience that trainees would normally have with us," explains Sanger.

"But for obvious reasons, it's been very difficult to arrange the international secondments that our trainees can apply to do in their second year of their training contract," she continues. "So, as an alternative, we substituted secondments to clients, which has worked well."

Most major law firms recruit their trainees whilst they are still at university, before they complete one or two years of further study at law school. "At Slaughter and May, it's

been business as usual for our trainee recruitment. We've not looked to reduce the number of graduates hired for the future, nor the number of trainees who started their training at the firm during the pandemic," says Sanger.

"Because we're recruiting our trainees at least two years in advance, we take a really long-term view," she continues. "And – just as we did in the midst of the global financial crisis of 2008 and 2009 – we've maintained all of our trainee hiring."

The firm typically recruits 80 graduates annually, with trainees starting at the firm in two intakes, in September and March each year. "Firms that cut their recruitment of trainees during a downturn often find that in the following years they don't have enough capacity when the economic situation improves," Sanger explains. "And one of the main reasons for continuing to take on the same number of new recruits is because we see our trainees as future partners of the firm, so we don't want to do anything that could impact that."

For the year ahead, Slaughter and May is hopeful that its trainees will be able to spend more time at the firm's offices, close to the Barbican in the City of London.

"The lockdowns brought more flexibility to everyone in the firm and enabled them to find a new routine that worked for them because, for example, they weren't commuting. But we know how keen many of our trainees have been to return to the office, particularly those who are flat sharing," reflects Sanger.

"Our new way of working will enable many of our people to continue on a flexible basis and spend up to 40% of the week at home, but we'll be expecting trainees to be in the office for 80% of the time," she concludes. "We know the trainee experience is definitely enriched from working closely with people in the office, for a good part of the week, and is really important for their learning."

NEWTON

Rani, Operations Consultant

WANT TO FEEL EMPOWERED LIKE RANI?

Then a career in consulting could be right for you. We're Newton Europe, an operational improvement consultancy with a twist. Since 2001, we've delivered real and sustainable change to industries far and wide with the help of people like Rani. She recently helped one of our clients create a new framework that streamlined their procurement process, and saved them over £70 million. She also set up the Women's Network at Newton, which has been instrumental in facilitating connections across our organisation. Rani attributes her success to the many words of encouragement she received from our directors. "If you have an idea," they told her, "just follow your heart."

Find out if a career in consulting is right for you at **WorkAtNewton.com**

NEVER NOT NEWTON

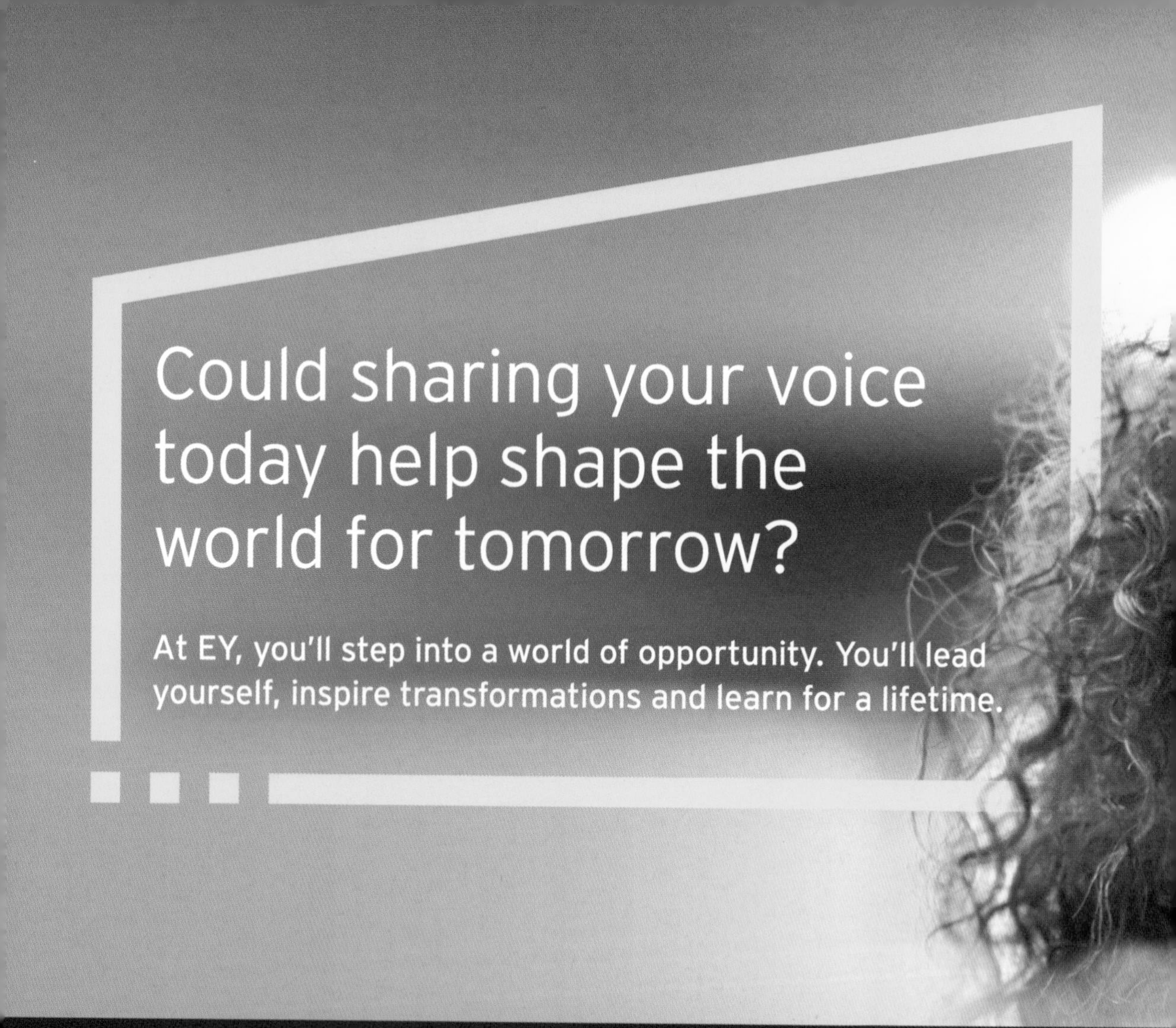

Could sharing your voice today help shape the world for tomorrow?

At EY, you'll step into a world of opportunity. You'll lead yourself, inspire transformations and learn for a lifetime.

We provide the tools, networks, experiences and opportunities to learn, lead, innovate, and grow. Open doors anywhere and drive positive impact everywhere. At EY, your career is yours to build.

Find out more about our world on page 118.

Our world. Your way.

The better the question. The better the answer.

EY
Building a better
working world

"

Working in the Technology Risk team at EY, I get to see at first hand
how quickly technology evolves. Here, we're encouraged to take each
day as an opportunity to lead, learn and transform. I work with a wide
range of local and global clients, industries, and projects. With each
project, I have unique opportunities to develop my skills and expertise,
all the while working alongside a talented and supportive team.

Shimona
Technology Risk Graduate

ey.com/uk/students

All of The Times for just £2.17 a month

Sign up to a student digital subscription for £26 a year and enjoy
unlimited access to The Times and The Sunday Times. That's a saving
of over 90% on the regular subscription rate of £26 per month.

Subscribe today at thetimes.co.uk/student

THE TIMES
THE SUNDAY TIMES
Know your times

EMPLOYER	RANK	Accountancy	Consulting	Engineering	Finance	General Management	Human Resources	Investment Banking	Law	Logistics	Marketing	Media	Property	Purchasing	Research & Development	Retail	Sales	Technology	Other	VACANCIES	Insight Courses	Degree Placements	Summer Internships	PAGE
KUBRICK	87		●															●		610				144
L'ORÉAL	21				●	●					●				●					30	●	●	●	146
LATHAM & WATKINS	98								●											24	●		●	148
LIDL	36				●	●				●			●	●		●				60+			●	150
LINKLATERS	19								●											100	●		●	152
LLOYDS BANKING GROUP	40	●		●	●						●							●		100+			●	154
MARS	82			●	●	●	●				●							●		25				156
MAZARS	99	●	●		●						●							●		250+		●	●	158
MI5	79				●	●	●											●	●	200+	●	●	●	160
MICROSOFT	47		●								●							●		45			●	162
MORGAN STANLEY	45				●			●	●									●	●	200+				164
MOTT MACDONALD	94		●	●									●					●		300				166
NATWEST GROUP	37				●			●										●		260+			●	168
NEWTON	44		●																	135				170
NGDP FOR LOCAL GOVERNMENT	50					●														150+				172
NHS	3	●			●	●	●													300				174
P&G	18			●	●						●	●		●			●			50		●	●	176
PENGUIN RANDOM HOUSE	31										●	●								200+			●	178
PEPSICO	92			●							●	●								15+		●	●	180
POLICE NOW	28																		●	400+				182
PWC	2	●	●		●				●									●		Around 1,200	●	●	●	184
ROLLS-ROYCE	26			●	●													●		No fixed quota				186
ROYAL NAVY	54			●	●	●	●		●	●		●			●			●		No fixed quota	●	●	●	188
RSM	97	●	●		●															390-400		●	●	190
SAVILLS	66												●							80+	●	●	●	192
SHELL	90			●	●	●	●				●							●		No fixed quota				194
SIEMENS	96			●	●	●												●		100+				196
SKY	33	●	●								●							●		170+	●			198
SLAUGHTER AND MAY	46								●											80	●		●	200
TEACH FIRST	9																		●	1,750	●			202
TESCO	41				●	●	●			●	●		●	●		●		●		100+			●	204
THG	72				●						●							●		250+	●	●	●	206
THINK AHEAD	39																		●	160			●	208
TPP	70										●							●		50+		●	●	210
UBS	59		●		●	●	●	●	●									●		100+	●	●	●	212
UNILEVER	16			●	●		●				●	●			●			●		40+		●	●	214
UNLOCKED	51																		●	130				216
VODAFONE	71				●	●	●										●	●		150-200		●	●	218
WELLCOME	81				●	●	●	●				●			●			●		12			●	220
WHITE & CASE	60								●											50	●	●	●	222

We only recruit one type of person

FEMALEBLACKMALE
ASIANSCHOOLLEAVER
GRADUATEDISABLED
GAYLOWINCOMEWHITE
TRANSGENDERCAREER
CHANGERNEURODIVERSE
BRITISHCITIZEN

At the UK intelligence services, we believe that with the right mix of minds, anything is possible. So, we don't recruit a particular 'type' of person. We need people who can bring a rich mix of skills, experiences and backgrounds to help us fight the threats we face.

Although each service has a slightly different remit, we all work towards one aim: protecting the UK and its people, at home and overseas. With a truly diverse workforce, we can keep the country safe.

MI5 protects the UK from threats to national security, such as terrorism and espionage. How? By gathering intelligence and working closely with our partners, we detect such threats and work out ways to stop them. Find us at: **www.mi5.gov.uk/careers**

MI6 works with the UK's foreign partners to support global stability by combating international terrorism and the spread of weapons. So, we work secretly around the world and in the UK, to stay ahead of our adversaries. Discover more: **www.sis.gov.uk**

GCHQ uses the ingenuity of our people and cutting-edge technology to protect the UK in the real world and online. That means we work with a wide range of partners to identify, analyse and stop cyber attacks, terrorism and serious crime. **www.gchq-careers.co.uk**

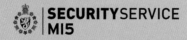

accenture

accenture.com/ukgrads

accentureETsupport@accenture.com ✉

Tomi – Analyst
Lakhy – Apprentice

Accenture is a global professional services company offering Strategy and Consulting, Interactive, Technology, and Operations services. Their 569,000 people deliver on the promise of technology and human ingenuity every day, serving clients in more than 120 countries.

Across 200 cities and 19 industries, Accenture works as one team with a common goal – embracing the power of change to create value and shared success for its clients, people, shareholders, partners, and communities.

As one of the world's leading consulting and technology organisations, Accenture examines a client's organisation to solve its toughest challenges – whether that's increasing profits, redefining strategies, innovating with the latest and greatest technologies, or offering better customer experiences. Accenture works with 91 of the Fortune Global 100 and, as of 2021, has made 19 consecutive appearances on the list of Fortune's World's Most Admired Companies.

Graduate programmes at Accenture present a world of opportunity at the heart of business transformation. With live project experience from the start, graduates will make an impact and develop rounded skills while enjoying a comprehensive induction, structured training, expert support, and great benefits. There's also a range of interest groups and networking options to get involved in.

Accenture is committed to a culture of inclusion and diversity, where everyone feels like they belong and innovation can truly be unleashed. This allows their people to perform at their very best and underpins a culture in which everyone feels they have an equal opportunity to build a career, advance, and thrive.

At the heart of every great change is a great human. Accenture looks for graduates from all degree disciplines with ideas, ingenuity, and a passion for making a difference.

GRADUATE VACANCIES IN 2022

CONSULTING
FINANCE
HUMAN RESOURCES
SALES
TECHNOLOGY

NUMBER OF VACANCIES
600+ graduate jobs

LOCATIONS OF VACANCIES

STARTING SALARY FOR 2022
£29,000-£33,500
Plus a sign-on bonus.

WORK EXPERIENCE
DEGREE PLACEMENTS | SUMMER INTERNSHIPS

UNIVERSITY PROMOTIONS DURING 2021-2022
ASTON, BATH, BIRMINGHAM, BRISTOL, CAMBRIDGE, CARDIFF, CITY, DURHAM, EDINBURGH, ESSEX, EXETER, GLASGOW, IMPERIAL COLLEGE LONDON, KING'S COLLEGE LONDON, LANCASTER, LEEDS, LSE, LOUGHBOROUGH, MANCHESTER, NEWCASTLE, NORTHUMBRIA, NOTTINGHAM, OXFORD, QMUL, READING, ROYAL HOLLOWAY, SHEFFIELD, SOUTHAMPTON, SURREY, UCL, WARWICK, YORK

MINIMUM ENTRY REQUIREMENTS
Any degree accepted

APPLICATION DEADLINE
Year-round recruitment
Early application is advised.

FURTHER INFORMATION
www.Top100GraduateEmployers.com
*Register now for the latest news, local promotions, work experience and graduate vacancies at **Accenture**.*

At the heart of every great change is a great human.

If you have ideas, ingenuity and a passion for making a difference, come and be a part of our team.

At Accenture, we believe that bringing together the different experiences and perspectives of our people allows us to create lasting and meaningful change for businesses, communities and society. You'll learn, grow and advance in a diverse culture of shared success, where you can bring your skills, curiosity and your best true self to your work.
Join us for the perfect blend of intensive training and live project experience, in a career where you'll match your ingenuity with the latest technology to do incredible things.

Learn more at accenture.com/ukgraduates

AECOM is the world's trusted infrastructure consulting firm, delivering professional services throughout the project lifecycle – from planning, design, and engineering to programme and construction management, on projects spanning transport, buildings, water, new energy, and the environment.

AECOM graduates make a real difference to both the built and natural environment. AECOM services include building engineering, environment, bridges, roads, rail, water, surveying, project management, planning, power, and architecture. Delivering clean water and energy. Building iconic skyscrapers. Planning new cities. Restoring damaged environments. Connecting people and economies with roads, bridges, tunnels and transit systems. Designing parks where children play.

Worldwide, AECOM designs, builds, finances, operates, and manages projects and programmes that unlock opportunities, protect the environment, and improve people's lives.

The AECOM Graduate Development Programme lasts for two years, and will provide graduates with full financial and development support towards their relevant professional qualification, including mentoring, residential training modules, an opportunity to work on live client projects, external training courses where required, and multi-disciplinary exposure.

AECOM is seeking applicants from around 35 disciplines, including civil, structural, mechanical, electrical, building services, fire and sustainable buildings engineering, as well as quantity & building surveying, project management, planning & design, acoustics, water & power related disciplines, and environment – including remediation, EIA, ecology, air quality, GIS, and much more.

GRADUATE VACANCIES IN 2022

CONSULTING
ENGINEERING
PROPERTY
TECHNOLOGY

NUMBER OF VACANCIES
350 graduate jobs

LOCATIONS OF VACANCIES

STARTING SALARY FOR 2022
£24,000-£28,000+

WORK EXPERIENCE

DEGREE PLACEMENTS | SUMMER INTERNSHIPS

UNIVERSITY PROMOTIONS DURING 2021-2022
ABERDEEN, ABERYSTWYTH, ASTON, BATH, BELFAST, BIRMINGHAM, BRADFORD, BRISTOL, BRUNEL, CAMBRIDGE, CARDIFF, CITY, DUNDEE, DURHAM, EDINBURGH, EXETER, GLASGOW, HERIOT-WATT, HULL, IMPERIAL COLLEGE LONDON, KING'S COLLEGE LONDON, KENT, LANCASTER, LEEDS, LEICESTER, LIVERPOOL, LSE, LOUGHBOROUGH, MANCHESTER, NEWCASTLE, NORTHUMBRIA, NOTTINGHAM, NOTTINGHAM TRENT, OXFORD, OXFORD BROOKES, PLYMOUTH, QMUL, READING, SHEFFIELD, SOUTHAMPTON, ST ANDREWS, STIRLING, STRATHCLYDE, SURREY, SUSSEX, SWANSEA, UEA, ULSTER, UCL, WARWICK, YORK

MINIMUM ENTRY REQUIREMENTS
2.1 Degree

APPLICATION DEADLINE
Year-round recruitment
Early application is advised.

FURTHER INFORMATION
www.Top100GraduateEmployers.com
Register now for the latest news, local promotions, work experience and graduate vacancies at AECOM.

I improve the energy performance of listed buildings

Meet Katie,
an engineering graduate at AECOM who is using building performance analysis software and energy models to inform different design options to improve the performance of listed buildings.

Find out how you can make an impact at

aecom.com/uk/impact

AIRBUS

Airbus is an international pioneer in the aerospace industry and a leader in designing, manufacturing, and delivering aerospace products, services, and solutions to customers on a global scale. Its aim is for a better-connected, safer, and more prosperous world.

Airbus graduates can take their first steps towards building a big career. Over the course of their programme, they can explore the breadth of the business through a series of three- to six-month rotational placements within disciplines such as engineering, finance, project management, business, and IT – allowing them to build the knowledge, experience, and understanding needed to progress within the organisation.

The Airbus UK graduate programme aims to accelerate learning development, helping graduates to discover new career paths and open their minds to the company's possibilities. It lasts between two and three years, and is both structured and flexible.

The placements are tailored to suit each graduate's needs, as well as those of the business, encouraging individuals to take control of their own career. Add to that outstanding training and development, a comprehensive induction, various technical and business modules, and graduates have everything they need to succeed in either their commercial aircraft or defence and space divisions. There is also the opportunity to take an optional Postgraduate Diploma in Engineering for further learning and development.

Airbus is a forward-thinking employer with a strong belief in a healthy work-life balance for its employees, and it supports flexible working. What's more, working alongside passionate and determined people, Airbus graduates will help to accomplish the extraordinary – on the ground, in the sky, and in space.

GRADUATE VACANCIES IN 2022
ENGINEERING
FINANCE
GENERAL MANAGEMENT
RESEARCH & DEVELOPMENT
TECHNOLOGY

NUMBER OF VACANCIES
TBC

LOCATIONS OF VACANCIES

STARTING SALARY FOR 2022
£27,000

WORK EXPERIENCE
DEGREE PLACEMENTS   SUMMER INTERNSHIPS

UNIVERSITY PROMOTIONS DURING 2021-2022
BATH, BRISTOL, IMPERIAL COLLEGE LONDON, LOUGHBOROUGH, MANCHESTER, SOUTHAMPTON, SWANSEA
Please check with your university careers service for full details of Airbus' local promotions and events.

MINIMUM ENTRY REQUIREMENTS
2.2 Degree

APPLICATION DEADLINE
TBC

FURTHER INFORMATION
www.Top100GraduateEmployers.com
Register now for the latest news, local promotions, work experience and graduate vacancies at Airbus.

Make your mark
Make it fly

We're looking for graduates with curiosity, drive and commitment who want to be part of a high-tech, innovative and global organisation. Our graduate and apprenticeship schemes will prepare you with the skills you need to progress and develop your talents. Together, we can achieve extraordinary things – on the ground, in the sky and in space.

At the forefront of innovation and a proven leader in global aerospace, Airbus designs, produces and delivers cutting-edge solutions that span Commercial Aircraft, Helicopters and Defence and Space - for a more connected, safer world.

Launch your career
airbus.com/careers

 linkedin.com/company/airbusgroup
 facebook.com/airbuscareers

 @AirbusCareers
 @WeAreAirbus

AIRBUS

Aldi came to the UK in 1990, and is now one of the UK's fastest-growing supermarkets and most successful retailers. As Aldi continues on an ambitious growth period, opening on average one store each week, employing the right people is key – without them, it wouldn't be possible.

All graduates enter the business on the Area Manager Training Programme, which has gained a reputation for offering an enormous amount of responsibility. Graduates get more than just a great salary and a fully expensed car. Over the 12 months, exceptional training and mentorship guides graduates on their way to managing approximately four stores. It's the perfect introduction to Aldi and a superb foundation for future success. Graduates will experience mind-stretching retail challenges that will sharpen their commercial edge and enable them to make critical business decisions later on in their journey.

After a few years in the role, graduates who show the willingness and drive to be flexible in both their location and areas of responsibility may get the chance to take on a project role within one of Aldi's Regions, National departments, Logistics, or even an International Secondment in countries such as the US or Australia. Further in the future, high-performing Area Managers could even move into a Director role within (for example) Buying, Finance, or Store Operations.

Aldi is built on an attitude. It's about never giving up; always striving for smarter, simpler ways of doing things. Aldi is a business with integrity – fair to partners and suppliers – and everything Aldi does is for the benefit of customers, colleagues and community.

Aldi looks for graduates who are incredibly hard-working, with a positive, 'roll their sleeves up' attitude. Aldi has so much more to offer – a rewarding and long-lasting career and the opportunity to contribute to the future success of Aldi.

GRADUATE VACANCIES IN 2022

GENERAL MANAGEMENT

RETAIL

NUMBER OF VACANCIES
100 graduate jobs

LOCATIONS OF VACANCIES

STARTING SALARY FOR 2022
£44,000

UNIVERSITY PROMOTIONS DURING 2021-2022
ASTON, BIRMINGHAM, CAMBRIDGE, CARDIFF, EDINBURGH, HULL, KING'S COLLEGE LONDON, LANCASTER, LEEDS, LIVERPOOL, LOUGHBOROUGH, MANCHESTER, NEWCASTLE, NORTHUMBRIA, NOTTINGHAM, SHEFFIELD, SOUTHAMPTON, ST ANDREWS, STRATHCLYDE, SURREY, SUSSEX, SWANSEA, YORK
Please check with your university careers service for full details of Aldi's local promotions and events.

MINIMUM ENTRY REQUIREMENTS
2.1 Degree, 96 UCAS points

APPLICATION DEADLINE
Year-round recruitment
Early application is advised.

FURTHER INFORMATION
www.Top100GraduateEmployers.com
Register now for the latest news, local promotions, work experience and graduate vacancies at Aldi.

MORE OPPORTUNITIES. MORE DETERMINATION.
MORE AMBITION. MORE FLEXIBILITY.

ALDIMEANSMORE

MORE MOTIVATION. MORE LEADERSHIP.
MORE CHALLENGES. MORE YOU.

Graduate Area Manager Programme

- £44,000 starting salary (rising to £79,040 after four years)
- BMW 3 series • Healthcare • Pension
- All-year round recruitment but places fill quickly

Discover more and apply at **aldirecruitment.co.uk/graduates**

#TeamAldi

Allen & Overy is a global law firm that helps the world's leading businesses to grow, innovate, and thrive. For almost a century, they have built a reputation for their commitment to think ahead and bring original solutions to their clients' most complex legal and commercial challenges.

At a time of significant turbulence in the business world, Allen & Overy are determined to help their clients embrace change, confidently expand into new markets, and keep on top of ever more complicated regulatory frameworks.

Allen & Overy is committed to being the world's most advanced law firm. Equipping clients to meet the demands of today's changing and challenging environment has prompted their growth into new complementary services. This includes delivering legal services in new and flexible ways, making the most of what legal tech has to offer, and providing specialist consulting and strategic advisory services to build strength and integrity into organisations. Allen & Overy now recruit at the graduate level for both Consulting and Law Tech, in addition to their Vacation Scheme and Training Contract vacancies.

The firm recognises that the world needs different. And it's by bringing together varied lived experiences, perspectives and thoughts that they generate ideas and build creative solutions. This is why Allen & Overy recruit students and graduates from all degree backgrounds.

As the world changes, the legal industry needs to evolve with it. Allen & Overy is investing in its people to ensure they have the skills and knowledge they will need to operate in the legal landscape of the future. They look for trainees who want to push the limits of law, and in return who can expect a rewarding experience that will prepare them for a career at the very pinnacle of the profession.

GRADUATE VACANCIES IN 2022

CONSULTING
LAW
TECHNOLOGY

NUMBER OF VACANCIES
80-90 graduate jobs

LOCATIONS OF VACANCIES

STARTING SALARY FOR 2022
£Competitive

WORK EXPERIENCE

| INSIGHT COURSES | SUMMER INTERNSHIPS |

UNIVERSITY PROMOTIONS DURING 2021-2022
Please check with your university careers service for full details of Allen & Overy's local promotions and events.

MINIMUM ENTRY REQUIREMENTS
2.1 Degree, 136 UCAS points

APPLICATION DEADLINE
Varies by function
Please see website for details.

FURTHER INFORMATION
www.Top100GraduateEmployers.com
Register now for the latest news, local promotions, work experience and graduate vacancies at Allen & Overy.

ALLEN & OVERY

The relentless pursuit of the next big breakthrough.
Transformation. Exhilaration.
Everything you need to get there.
IT'S TIME.

The world is changing more than ever before. And not only do we need to change with it, but we need to help shape its new form. At Allen & Overy, it's our mission to be at the cutting edge of the legal industry. This is your chance to be part of something revolutionary, to make your mark and lead the way.

Amazon's mission is "to be Earth's most customer-centric company", and the Operations team is at the heart of that mission. Supported by innovative, world-class technologies, the global network of Fulfillment Centers (FCs) and delivery stations are dedicated to supporting customers worldwide.

Every year, Amazon offers hundreds of graduates the opportunity to design their path to a successful career. Starting from Day 1, graduates are given a leadership position with significant responsibilities. Amazon believes in hiring and developing the best; their graduates are given numerous opportunities to acquire technical skills that will enable them to take on future opportunities within the company. Inventing and delivering things that were never thought possible isn't easy, but Amazon embraces this challenge every day. By working on behalf of its customers, Amazon is building the future – one innovative product, service, and idea at a time. It's the job of Amazon employees to make bold bets. Success is measured against the possible, not the probable.

Amazon encourages graduates to have a self-starter mentality when it comes to learning, and they supplement this with hands-on training to enable their people to progress and succeed. There are opportunities across a broad spectrum of teams, and many of its graduates join the organisation as Area Managers, who – right from Day 1 – are given significant responsibility to lead and develop teams. The company hires the brightest minds and offers them the platform to think around corners and innovate on behalf of their customers.

Amazon is an equal opportunities employer and believes passionately that employing a diverse workforce is central to success. Recruiting decisions are based on having the experience, skills, and passion to discover, invent, simplify, and build.

GRADUATE VACANCIES IN 2022
ENGINEERING
FINANCE
GENERAL MANAGEMENT
HUMAN RESOURCES
LOGISTICS
PURCHASING
TECHNOLOGY

NUMBER OF VACANCIES
800+ graduate jobs

LOCATIONS OF VACANCIES

Vacancies also available in Europe.

STARTING SALARY FOR 2022
£Competitive
Plus relocation, sign-on, and shares bonuses.

WORK EXPERIENCE
SUMMER INTERNSHIPS

UNIVERSITY PROMOTIONS DURING 2021-2022
ASTON, BATH, BIRMINGHAM, BRISTOL, CAMBRIDGE, CARDIFF, CITY, DURHAM, EDINBURGH, EXETER, GLASGOW, IMPERIAL COLLEGE LONDON, KING'S COLLEGE LONDON, LANCASTER, LEEDS, LIVERPOOL, LOUGHBOROUGH, MANCHESTER, NEWCASTLE, NOTTINGHAM, OXFORD, READING, SHEFFIELD, SOUTHAMPTON, ST ANDREWS, STRATHCLYDE, UCL, WARWICK, YORK

MINIMUM ENTRY REQUIREMENTS
Any degree accepted

APPLICATION DEADLINE
Year-round recruitment
Early application is advised.

FURTHER INFORMATION
www.Top100GraduateEmployers.com
Register now for the latest news, local promotions, work experience and graduate vacancies at Amazon.

We are hiring
800+ Graduates

Build your future in
Amazon Operations

ARMY
BE THE BEST

FIND WHERE YOU BELONG
SEARCH ARMY OFFICER

ARMY
BE THE BEST

Lead from the front, do something that really matters, and serve the nation. Officers in the British Army have the responsibility of leading their soldiers to help make the world a safer, better place. The rewards are exceptional, the challenge is incredible, and there's no bigger adventure in life.

The journey to becoming a British Army Officer begins at the Royal Military Academy Sandhurst, where Officer Cadets learn all the skills they need – from weapons handling to outdoor survival – and discover what it takes to lead their team and be responsible for the safety of the nation. Then, once they commission, they take command of a platoon of up to 30 soldiers and start the specialist training they need to be experts in their role – whether that's engineering, intelligence gathering, or piloting an Apache helicopter.

From parachuting in the UK to sub-aqua diving overseas, Army Officers live an adventurous life, and take part in training around the world, all whilst earning a competitive salary. There are many benefits that come with Army life, from sports and state-of-the-art training facilities to gaining professional qualifications and continually progressing their career. The Army also provides financial support for its future leaders, offering Army Undergraduate Bursaries to those who are interested in a career as an Army Officer after university, including a range of bursaries available for students of technical disciplines.

The Army looks for leadership potential, a sense of purpose, and the drive to succeed. From the moment Officer Cadets join, they're set on a clear path for promotion and progression. With world-class leadership training and continuous support, Army Officers rise through the ranks to become influential leaders. Their life is full of challenge and adventure, and it's a place where they can truly make a difference.

GRADUATE VACANCIES IN 2022

ENGINEERING
GENERAL MANAGEMENT
HUMAN RESOURCES
LAW
LOGISTICS
TECHNOLOGY

NUMBER OF VACANCIES
650+ graduate jobs

LOCATIONS OF VACANCIES

STARTING SALARY FOR 2022
Around £33,000
After training.

UNIVERSITY PROMOTIONS DURING 2021-2022
ABERDEEN, ABERYSTWYTH, ASTON, BIRMINGHAM, BRADFORD, BRUNEL, CAMBRIDGE, CARDIFF, DUNDEE, DURHAM, EDINBURGH, ESSEX, EXETER, GLASGOW, HERIOT-WATT, HULL, KING'S COLLEGE LONDON, KENT, LANCASTER, LEEDS, LEICESTER, LIVERPOOL, LOUGHBOROUGH, MANCHESTER, NEWCASTLE, NORTHUMBRIA, NOTTINGHAM, NOTTINGHAM TRENT, OXFORD, OXFORD BROOKES, PLYMOUTH, SHEFFIELD, UEA, ULSTER, WARWICK, YORK
Please check with your university careers service for full details of the British Army's local promotions and events.

MINIMUM ENTRY REQUIREMENTS
72 UCAS points
180 UCAS points for those who passed exams before 2017.

APPLICATION DEADLINE
Year-round recruitment

FURTHER INFORMATION
www.Top100GraduateEmployers.com
Register now for the latest news, local promotions, work experience and graduate vacancies at the British Army.

THIS IS BELONGING

The chance to do something that matters. Make your family proud as you make a difference to the world. Lead a team. As a British Army Officer, you'll live a life full of adventure and accomplishment. Your career has no limits, and with the opportunity to gain qualifications and adaptable skills, you'll become an incredible leader. You'll be awarded a starting salary of around £27,000, which will rise to around £33,000 upon completion of one year's training – and as you advance through the ranks, so will your salary.

Travel the world and lead your soldiers as you play a vital part in creating a sense of belonging that empowers all. We realise your potential and will support you to reach it.

Find where you belong.

SEARCH
ARMY OFFICER

ARMY
BE THE BEST

careers.astrazeneca.com/early-talent

facebook.com/AstraZenecaCareers **f**

linkedin.com/company/astrazeneca **in**   twitter.com/AstraZenecaJobs **𝕐**

instagram.com/AstraZeneca **⊙**   youtube.com/AstraZeneca **▶**

AstraZeneca is a global, science-led, patient-focused biopharmaceutical company employing 70,000 people worldwide. They focus on the discovery, development, and commercialisation of prescription medicines for some of the world's most serious diseases.

AstraZeneca's graduate programmes cover a broad range of functions and specialities. They open many doors, and will kickstart a graduate's career. Graduates are empowered to jump in, take the initiative, be part of meaningful project teams, and make an impact by delivering real value for their patients and the business.

Their programmes place an emphasis on personal and professional development, and they invest in each graduate's unique interests and potential. Working in a fast-paced yet deeply supportive and collaborative environment, graduates are encouraged to take responsibility and put their knowledge into practice, whilst being guided and supported by inspiring peers.

AstraZeneca's graduates have significant opportunities to build bonds with their international peers, developing connections and growing their network with early talent, experts, and leaders across the business.

The pace is quick and challenging, but graduates always have the help and encouragement they need to set them up for success, achieve their goals, and have fun doing it.

AstraZeneca is proud of their award-winning, progressive working practices. They welcome diverse thinking, curiosity, collaboration, and the courage to go further, together. To find out more about what makes them unique and becoming a part of their team, visit the early talent pages of their global careers website.

GRADUATE VACANCIES IN 2022
ENGINEERING
FINANCE
GENERAL MANAGEMENT
HUMAN RESOURCES
LOGISTICS
PURCHASING
RESEARCH & DEVELOPMENT
TECHNOLOGY

NUMBER OF VACANCIES
90+ graduate jobs

LOCATIONS OF VACANCIES

Vacancies also available in Europe, the USA, and elsewhere in the world.

STARTING SALARY FOR 2022
£31,000+
Plus an annual bonus and flexible benefits package.

WORK EXPERIENCE
| DEGREE PLACEMENTS | SUMMER INTERNSHIPS |

UNIVERSITY PROMOTIONS DURING 2021-2022
BIRMINGHAM, BRISTOL, CAMBRIDGE, CARDIFF, EDINBURGH, KING'S COLLEGE LONDON, LANCASTER, LEEDS, LEICESTER, LIVERPOOL, MANCHESTER, NOTTINGHAM, QMUL, SHEFFIELD, UCL, WARWICK, YORK

MINIMUM ENTRY REQUIREMENTS
2.1 Degree

APPLICATION DEADLINE
Varies by function

FURTHER INFORMATION
www.Top100GraduateEmployers.com
*Register now for the latest news, local promotions, work experience and graduate vacancies at **AstraZeneca**.*

AstraZeneca

Make an impact and kickstart your career

We have exciting and rewarding Graduate Programmes in:

- Biometrics & Information Sciences
- BioPharmaceutical Development
- Data Sciences & Artificial Intelligence
- Human Resources
- IT/Technology Leadership
- Operations & Supply Chain
- Pharmaceutical Technology & Development
- Research & Development

Starting salary for 2022

£31,000+

Plus bonus, benefits
& relocation (if applicable)

*AstraZeneca is an equal
opportunity employer*

For more information and to apply, please visit:
careers.astrazeneca.com/early-talent

BAE SYSTEMS

BAE Systems helps to protect people and national security, critical infrastructure and vital information. It's a culture that values diversity, rewards integrity and merit, and is a place where everyone has the opportunity to fulfil their potential, no matter what their background.

With a workforce of 90,000 people in more than 40 countries, BAE Systems is committed to nurturing talent and developing highly skilled colleagues – empowering their people to drive innovation, make the right decisions, and solve complex challenges. With a long history of innovation and excellence behind them, and ambitious plans for the future, BAE Systems is a place graduates and undergraduates can start and grow their career with confidence.

Wherever their career interests lie – from engineering, finance, or project management, to manufacturing, consulting, technology, or wider business disciplines – at BAE Systems, graduates have the chance to make a real impact, where it counts, whichever team they join.

With opportunities nationwide, joining a BAE Systems programme means learning through valuable hands-on experience and formal training – developing a career, from day one. On completing the graduate programme, and demonstrating the passion and potential to lead, graduates could even find themselves on BAE Systems' Future Talent Programme, helping the organisation to meet its most significant business challenges.

BAE Systems is not just proud of what they do, they're proud of how they do it. New graduates will be part of a culture that's committed to working to the highest ethical and environmental standards, in an inclusive work environment, making a positive contribution to the countries and communities in which they operate. Make a difference – apply now.

GRADUATE VACANCIES IN 2022
CONSULTING
ENGINEERING
FINANCE
GENERAL MANAGEMENT
HUMAN RESOURCES
MARKETING
SALES
TECHNOLOGY

NUMBER OF VACANCIES
Around 300 graduate jobs

LOCATIONS OF VACANCIES

STARTING SALARY FOR 2022
£30,000

WORK EXPERIENCE
| DEGREE PLACEMENTS | SUMMER INTERNSHIPS |

UNIVERSITY PROMOTIONS DURING 2021-2022
ASTON, BATH, BIRMINGHAM, BRISTOL, BRUNEL, EDINBURGH, GLASGOW, IMPERIAL COLLEGE LONDON, KENT, LANCASTER, LEICESTER, LIVERPOOL, LOUGHBOROUGH, MANCHESTER, NEWCASTLE, NOTTINGHAM, QUEEN MARY LONDON, SHEFFIELD, SOUTHAMPTON, STRATHCLYDE, SURREY, UNIVERSITY COLLEGE LONDON, WARWICK
Please check with your university careers service for full details of BAE Systems' local promotions and events.

MINIMUM ENTRY REQUIREMENTS
Varies by function
Relevant degree required for some roles.

APPLICATION DEADLINE
Varies by function

FURTHER INFORMATION
www.Top100GraduateEmployers.com
Register now for the latest news, local promotions, work experience and graduate vacancies at BAE Systems.

Accelerate your career where it counts

baesystems.com/graduates

This is a place for career-builders, smart-thinkers and curious minds. This is where you'll find yourself, surprise yourself, become an expert in your field. With a long history of innovation and excellence behind us, and ambitious plans for the future – this is a place you can start, and grow your career with confidence.

As a BAE Systems trainee, you'll play an important part in serving, supplying and protecting those who serve and protect us. You'll be empowered to be your best, whichever area you choose to join us - from project management, technology or engineering, to finance, consulting or manufacturing – we have a range of roles to suit everyone.

Ours is an inclusive and supportive environment – so no matter what your background, you'll have all the opportunities you need to succeed.

Join us, this is a place where you'll make a real difference.

baesystems.com/graduates

BAE SYSTEMS

With over 13,000 people in 78 offices around the world, Baker McKenzie prides itself on being a truly innovative law firm. In the current climate, that's never been more important. It also enables them to go above and beyond for their clients, collaborating across borders, markets, and industries.

Working at Baker McKenzie means being challenged. It means being supported. Yes, they're a big firm, but they're not so big that they fail to recognise the importance of diverse talent.

As a Trainee Solicitor, graduates will liaise directly with clients on high-profile cases. They'll sit in on important meetings and prepare agreements, deeds, and other legal documents. They'll also get the chance to apply for a six-month secondment at one of Baker McKenzie's international offices. Past trainees have spent time in San Francisco, Singapore, Brussels, New York, and Tokyo. They've worked with big-name debt funds and large banks on deals which make the six o'clock news.

When it comes to diversity and inclusion, the firm invests in a number of employee networks committed to mental health, LGBT+ rights, cultural diversity, social mobility, and more. And when it comes to culture, Baker McKenzie promotes a positive working environment where creativity is encouraged and different points of view are heard. The firm also has its own football, netball, cricket, and mixed hockey teams. Yoga classes are held at lunchtimes and in the evenings and, to help employees get to know each other away from their desks, Baker McKenzie also arranges regular social events.

Diversity is central to the firm's success. They feel at home anywhere in the world and rely on their people to navigate cultures, borders, and practices with ease.

GRADUATE VACANCIES IN 2022
LAW

NUMBER OF VACANCIES
33 graduate jobs
For training contracts starting in 2024.

LOCATIONS OF VACANCIES

STARTING SALARY FOR 2022
£48,000

WORK EXPERIENCE
INSIGHT COURSES | SUMMER INTERNSHIPS

UNIVERSITY PROMOTIONS DURING 2021-2022
ABERDEEN, BATH, BELFAST, BIRMINGHAM, BRISTOL, CAMBRIDGE, CARDIFF, DURHAM, EDINBURGH, ESSEX, EXETER, GLASGOW, KING'S COLLEGE LONDON, KENT, LANCASTER, LEEDS, LEICESTER, LIVERPOOL, LONDON SCHOOL OF ECONOMICS, MANCHESTER, NEWCASTLE, NOTTINGHAM, OXFORD, QUEEN MARY LONDON, SOUTHAMPTON, ST ANDREWS, SWANSEA, UEA, UNIVERSITY COLLEGE LONDON, WARWICK, YORK
Please check with your university careers service for full details of Baker McKenzie's local promotions and events.

MINIMUM ENTRY REQUIREMENTS
2.1 Degree

APPLICATION DEADLINE
Year-round recruitment
Early application is advised.

FURTHER INFORMATION
www.Top100GraduateEmployers.com
Register now for the latest news, local promotions, work experience and graduate vacancies at Baker McKenzie.

BANK OF AMERICA

campus.bankofamerica.com

juniortalentemea@bofa.com

linkedin.com/company/bank-of-america | twitter.com/BankofAmerica

instagram.com/BankofAmerica | youtube.com/BankofAmerica

One of the world's leading financial institutions, Bank of America serves 66 million customers, from individuals to small businesses, governments, and large corporations. A 200,000-strong workforce in more than 35 countries helps to make customers' lives better.

Bank of America believes it's important to work for what matters. To that end, graduates work in a collaborative environment with real responsibilities from day one and plenty of opportunities to shape a meaningful career.

Bank of America cares deeply about the planet and the people on it. From a $1.25 billion, five-year commitment to help address economic and racial inequality to getting to Zero Greenhouse Gas Emissions by 2050, responsible investing drives the business. Together with its graduates, Bank of America wants to shape a better world – one that's smarter, greener, safer, and more inclusive. Specifically, the worlds of sustainable finance, workplace culture, and technology.

There are many opportunities to lead change, and graduates can shape a career in a range of areas: Compliance, Corporate Audit, Corporate Treasury, Global Corporate & Investment Banking Credit, Global Corporate & Investment Banking, Global Markets, Global Research, Global Transaction Services, Market Risk, Quantitative Management, and Technology.

Bank of America cares deeply about shaping the world of work to be an equal and inclusive one. In April 2021, the bank was named one of Fortune Magazine's "100 Best Companies to Work For".

Applicants from all backgrounds are welcome – with a focus on attracting, retaining, and developing diverse talent, in order to mirror the customers, clients, and communities that Bank of America serve.

GRADUATE VACANCIES IN 2022

ACCOUNTANCY
FINANCE
INVESTMENT BANKING
TECHNOLOGY

NUMBER OF VACANCIES
No fixed quota

LOCATIONS OF VACANCIES

Vacancies also available in Europe.

STARTING SALARY FOR 2022
£Competitive
Plus a competitive bonus.

WORK EXPERIENCE
DEGREE PLACEMENTS | SUMMER INTERNSHIPS

UNIVERSITY PROMOTIONS DURING 2021-2022
BANGOR, BATH, BIRMINGHAM, BRISTOL, CAMBRIDGE, CARDIFF, CITY, DURHAM, EDINBURGH, EXETER, HULL, IMPERIAL COLLEGE LONDON, KING'S COLLEGE LONDON, LANCASTER, LEEDS, LEICESTER, LIVERPOOL, LSE, LOUGHBOROUGH, MANCHESTER, NEWCASTLE, NOTTINGHAM, OXFORD, QMUL, READING, ROYAL HOLLOWAY, SHEFFIELD, SOUTHAMPTON, ST ANDREWS, SURREY, UCL, WARWICK, YORK

MINIMUM ENTRY REQUIREMENTS
2.1 Degree, 112 UCAS points
280 UCAS points for those who passed exams before 2017.

APPLICATION DEADLINE
Varies by function

FURTHER INFORMATION
www.Top100GraduateEmployers.com
Register now for the latest news, local promotions, work experience and graduate vacancies at Bank of America.

BARCLAYS

Barclays is a British universal bank, diversified by business, by different types of customers and clients, and by geography. Barclays' global businesses include consumer banking and payments operations, as well as a top-tier, full service corporate and investment bank with a heritage of success.

Joining Barclays as a graduate or intern means the opportunity to do truly meaningful work, to discover a financial company that's focused on a better future for everyone, and to develop skills that will pave the way for a career that's both challenging and inspiring.

Spanning everything from Technology to Investment Banking, Barclays' two global graduate programmes will either develop graduates into a technical expert in their chosen field or help to build an extraordinary depth and breadth of experience through a deep dive into a chosen business area. Meanwhile, interns at the bank are immersed in real projects with real outcomes.

At Barclays, graduates and interns help to shape the future. The bank has a legacy of innovation, from introducing the first ATMs to launching contactless payments. Today, that forward-thinking approach continues. Barclays is committed to being a net zero bank by 2050, for example, and is experimenting with emerging technologies like blockchain and quantum computing.

Those joining can expect immediate responsibility, exciting collaborations, and ongoing training. This means Barclays looks for graduates with an innate sense of curiosity, along with the agility and adaptability it takes to come up with new ideas that can become ground-breaking.

With an inclusive culture, Barclays welcomes people from all walks of life. Whoever graduates are and wherever they want to get to, there really are no limits as to what they can do, what they can discover, and how fast they develop.

GRADUATE VACANCIES IN 2022
ACCOUNTANCY
ENGINEERING
FINANCE
HUMAN RESOURCES
INVESTMENT BANKING
MARKETING
RESEARCH & DEVELOPMENT
SALES
TECHNOLOGY

NUMBER OF VACANCIES
500+ graduate jobs

LOCATIONS OF VACANCIES

Vacancies also available worldwide.

STARTING SALARY FOR 2022
£Competitive
Graduates receive scholarship and bursary payment.

WORK EXPERIENCE
| INSIGHT COURSES | DEGREE PLACEMENTS | SUMMER INTERNSHIPS |

UNIVERSITY PROMOTIONS DURING 2021-2022
BATH, BIRMINGHAM, BRISTOL, CAMBRIDGE, DURHAM, EDINBURGH, GLASGOW, HERIOT-WATT, IMPERIAL COLLEGE LONDON, KING'S COLLEGE LONDON, LONDON SCHOOL OF ECONOMICS, MANCHESTER, NOTTINGHAM, OXFORD, QUEEN MARY LONDON, ST ANDREWS, STRATHCLYDE, WARWICK
Please check with your university careers service for full details of Barclays' local promotions and events.

APPLICATION DEADLINE
Varies by function

FURTHER INFORMATION
www.Top100GraduateEmployers.com
*Register now for the latest news, local promotions, work experience and graduate vacancies at **Barclays**.*

DO, DISCOVER, DEVELOP.

Join Barclays as a graduate or intern, and you'll do work that challenges you, discover opportunities to stretch you and develop innovations that excite you. You'll enjoy the kind of training that will bring out the best in you. And you'll be empowered to discover your full potential.

**To find out more, type
search.jobs.barclays**

 BARCLAYS

BBC

The BBC is the world's leading public service broadcaster, creating distinctive, world-class programmes and content which inform, educate, and entertain millions of people in the UK and around the world. More than 20,000 staff work at the BBC in journalism, production, engineering, technology, and corporate services.

The BBC provides a wide range of programmes, content, and services for audiences across the UK on television, radio, and digitally.

Opportunities for graduates are available across most areas, with a strong focus on potential rather than the level of academic achievement.

Graduate and postgraduate apprenticeships and trainee schemes are available in Journalism, Content Production, Production Management, Broadcast Engineering, Software Engineering, Research and Development, UX Design, and Communications. Graduates should expect a mix of placements and training periods, working on shows, products, and services that are enjoyed every day by millions of people.

Attitude, curiosity, and passion impress BBC recruiters, as does a good dose of life experience and the ability to communicate, work in a team, and innovate. New perspectives are important to the BBC, and competition for places is tough. Being able to demonstrate motivation for the role through extracurricular activities is really important.

Recruitment takes place at various times throughout the year; the BBC's careers website details the apprenticeship and trainee programmes available for 2022, including expected open dates for applications. New opportunities do spring up throughout the year though, so interested students should register for email alerts on the BBC's careers site to ensure they are kept up to date. Most apprenticeship and trainee programmes start in September.

GRADUATE VACANCIES IN 2022

ENGINEERING

MEDIA

RESEARCH & DEVELOPMENT

TECHNOLOGY

NUMBER OF VACANCIES
100+ graduate jobs

LOCATIONS OF VACANCIES

STARTING SALARY FOR 2022
£21,216

WORK EXPERIENCE
SUMMER INTERNSHIPS

UNIVERSITY PROMOTIONS DURING 2021-2022
Please check with your university careers service for full details of the BBC's local promotions and events.

MINIMUM ENTRY REQUIREMENTS
Varies by function

APPLICATION DEADLINE
Varies by function

FURTHER INFORMATION
www.Top100GraduateEmployers.com
Register now for the latest news, local promotions, work experience and graduate vacancies at the BBC.

Be part of something special. Join the BBC.

Opportunities in Broadcast Engineering, Software Engineering, Research & Development, User Experience, Journalism, Production and more.

To find out more, visit bbc.co.uk/youmakethebbc

BDO is one of the UK's largest accountancy and business advisory firms, providing the solutions that ambitious and entrepreneurial businesses need to navigate today's changing world. The BDO global network provides advisory services in 167 countries, with 91,000 people worldwide.

When the most innovative and high-growth businesses need advice on accountancy and business, they turn to BDO. With expertise across Financial Services, Healthcare, Leisure & Hospitality, Retail, Manufacturing, Technology, Media, Not-for-Profit, Public Sector, and many more industries, BDO provide the advice and answers that help AIM-listed companies achieve their aspirations.

Specialising in Tax, Audit & Assurance, Advisory, and Business Services & Outsourcing, BDO's graduate programmes are for those who want to work with high-profile clients, on challenging work, from day one.

They look for trainees who want to bring themselves to everything they do. Those who are prepared to ask questions, offer up ideas, and seize every opportunity. Those who have a drive to inspire more conversations and build lasting relationships. And, in return, BDO will provide a breadth of experience and opportunities to develop skills that few could match.

Study for professional qualifications like the ACA, CFA, and CTA to become an expert in a chosen area. At BDO, trainees are shaped into the independent and ethical advisors the UK's most forward-thinking businesses rely on. With early exposure to clients, trainees experience varied work that will broaden their horizons. BDO provides expert coaching and mentoring at every step, so that trainees can build a career with confidence.

Want to work at the very heart of accountancy and business? Set a course for a rewarding career, with a role at BDO.

GRADUATE VACANCIES IN 2022
ACCOUNTANCY
FINANCE

NUMBER OF VACANCIES
600 graduate jobs

LOCATIONS OF VACANCIES

STARTING SALARY FOR 2022
£Competitive
Plus a range of benefits.

WORK EXPERIENCE

INSIGHT COURSES	DEGREE PLACEMENTS	SUMMER INTERNSHIPS

UNIVERSITY PROMOTIONS DURING 2021-2022
ABERDEEN, ASTON, BATH, BIRMINGHAM, BRISTOL, CAMBRIDGE, CITY, DURHAM, EDINBURGH, ESSEX, EXETER, GLASGOW, HERIOT-WATT, IMPERIAL COLLEGE LONDON, KING'S COLLEGE LONDON, KENT, LANCASTER, LEEDS, LEICESTER, LIVERPOOL, LONDON SCHOOL OF ECONOMICS, LOUGHBOROUGH, MANCHESTER, NEWCASTLE, NOTTINGHAM, OXFORD, READING, ROYAL HOLLOWAY, SHEFFIELD, SOUTHAMPTON, ST ANDREWS, STIRLING, STRATHCLYDE, SURREY, SUSSEX, UEA, UNIVERSITY COLLEGE LONDON, WARWICK, YORK
Please check with your university careers service for full details of BDO's local promotions and events.

MINIMUM ENTRY REQUIREMENTS
2.2 Degree
Any degree discipline accepted.

APPLICATION DEADLINE
Year-round recruitment
Early application is advised.

FURTHER INFORMATION
www.Top100GraduateEmployers.com
Register now for the latest news, local promotions, work experience and graduate vacancies at BDO.

FIND MORE THAN A CHANCE TO SHINE

FIND YOUR FUTURE

We're all about helping people and businesses succeed. So, if you're looking for somewhere you can be yourself and grow your career at the same time, BDO is the place for you.

On our graduate programme, you'll experience real responsibility and purpose from day one. Working with people who value your ideas and invest in your success, you'll be helping to solve complex client challenges while earning a respected qualification. And with exposure to a range of industries across the UK and beyond, you'll be able to start building a powerful network to maximise your personal and professional growth.

We accept any degree discipline – you won't need an accounting or finance degree to join us. Whether it's Audit, Tax, Advisory or Business Services & Outsourcing, we'll give you all you need to succeed.

Start your career today
bdoearlyincareer.co.uk

EMEAcampusrecruitment@blackrock.com

twitter.com/BlackRock   facebook.com/BlackRock

instagram.com/BlackRock   linkedin.com/company/blackrock

BlackRock

BlackRock's purpose is to help more and more people experience financial wellbeing. As a global investment manager and a leading provider of financial technology, their clients – from grandparents, doctors, and teachers to large institutions – turn to them for the solutions needed when planning for their most important goals.

BlackRock is building a culture of innovation, curiosity, and collaboration, one that enables every employee to be themselves and to be valued for it. Being a part of BlackRock means being a part of a community of smart, ambitious people. BlackRock values diversity of thought and background, and believes everyone has a voice at the table. No matter what level, employees are given real responsibility from day one – and BlackRock is looking for future colleagues to help challenge the status quo.

BlackRock brings together financial leadership, worldwide reach, and state-of the-art technology to provide answers to the millions of investors who entrust their financial futures to the company.

The story of BlackRock's success rests not just with its founders but with the thousands of talented people who have brought their ideas and energy to the firm every day since. BlackRock believes that the challenges of a diverse world require the innovations of a diverse company. That's why BlackRock is looking for fresh ideas and viewpoints. BlackRock knows that its success depends on its ability to use collective experiences and ideas to achieve more for clients and the business.

At BlackRock, students can have a career that's exciting, rewarding, and full of possibilities and opportunities. BlackRock offers roles in advisory services; analytics & risk; business management & strategy; business operations; finance & internal audit; investments; compliance; marketing & communications; sales & relationship management; and technology.

GRADUATE VACANCIES IN 2022

ACCOUNTANCY
CONSULTING
ENGINEERING
FINANCE
INVESTMENT BANKING
MARKETING
PURCHASING
SALES
TECHNOLOGY

NUMBER OF VACANCIES
140 graduate jobs

LOCATIONS OF VACANCIES

Vacancies also available in Europe, the USA, and Asia.

STARTING SALARY FOR 2022
£Competitive
Plus a sign-on bonus – amount and currency based on the offer location.

WORK EXPERIENCE

DEGREE PLACEMENTS	SUMMER INTERNSHIPS

UNIVERSITY PROMOTIONS DURING 2021-2022
Please check with your university careers service for full details of BlackRock's local promotions and events.

MINIMUM ENTRY REQUIREMENTS
Varies by function
Relevant degree required for some roles.

APPLICATION DEADLINE
Varies by function

FURTHER INFORMATION
www.Top100GraduateEmployers.com
Register now for the latest news, local promotions, work experience and graduate vacancies at BlackRock.

Discover a different path

BlackRock is a global investment firm, trusted to manage more assets than any other. We're responsible for the financial wellbeing of governments, foundations, and people saving for retirement, their children's education and hopes of a better life. Which gets to our purpose. We help more and more people experience financial wellbeing.

BlackRock employees from around the globe are students of the market and students of technology, respectfully anti-bureaucratic, and innovative at the core. If that sounds like you, discover a different path at:
careers.blackrock.com/early-careers

BlackRock.

Bloomberg

As a global information and technology company, Bloomberg uses its dynamic network of data, ideas, and analysis to solve difficult problems every day. Its customers around the world rely on them to deliver accurate, real-time business and market information that helps them make important financial decisions.

Bloomberg is guided by four core values: innovation, collaboration, customer service, and doing the right thing. The European Headquarters in London, one of the world's most sustainable office buildings, is a testament to that innovation.

Bloomberg offers internship and full-time entry-level roles at their London office across a range of business areas including Analytics & Sales, Engineering, Global Data, Operations, and more. Candidates who join Bloomberg can build and define their own unique career, rather than a pre-defined path. Bloomberg is proud to have a truly global dynamic organisation, so all employees are empowered to have an impact and are measured by their contributions. All graduate starters will participate in team-specific training that continues throughout their career via robust career development resources.

Bloomberg also offers internships to provide an unparalleled combination of learning, networking, and project responsibilities. The internship programme aims to provide first-hand exposure to its business and unique culture, and is filled with training, seminars, senior leader speaker series, philanthropic events, and more.

Candidates apply online on Bloomberg's career website. The interview process will depend on the business area they have applied to, but it typically involves a video and/or telephone interview followed by in-person interviews and assessment days. Bloomberg hire on a rolling basis, so early application is advised.

GRADUATE VACANCIES IN 2022

ENGINEERING

FINANCE

SALES

TECHNOLOGY

NUMBER OF VACANCIES
350+ graduate jobs

LOCATIONS OF VACANCIES

STARTING SALARY FOR 2022
£Competitive
Plus a competitive bonus.

WORK EXPERIENCE
INSIGHT COURSES   SUMMER INTERNSHIPS

UNIVERSITY PROMOTIONS DURING 2021-2022
BATH, CAMBRIDGE, EDINBURGH, IMPERIAL COLLEGE LONDON, KING'S COLLEGE LONDON, LONDON SCHOOL OF ECONOMICS, MANCHESTER, OXFORD, QUEEN MARY LONDON, SOUTHAMPTON, UNIVERSITY COLLEGE LONDON, WARWICK
Please check with your university careers service for full details of Bloomberg's local promotions and events.

APPLICATION DEADLINE
Year-round recruitment

FURTHER INFORMATION
www.Top100GraduateEmployers.com
Register now for the latest news, local promotions, work experience and graduate vacancies at **Bloomberg**.

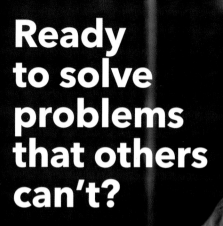

Ready to solve problems that others can't?

At Bloomberg, we find answers and make connections that improve our world. It's our purpose. What's yours?

bloomberg.com/careers

Bloomberg

Make connections **on purpose.**

BCG

careers.bcg.com

facebook.com/BCGinUK

linkedin.com/company/boston-consulting-group   twitter.com/BCG

instagram.com/BCGinUK   youtube.com/TheBostonConsultingGroup

When organisations find problems they can't solve on their own, that's where BCG gets to work. As the pioneer in business strategy consulting, it has been helping to solve some of the world's biggest problems since it was founded nearly 60 years ago. Today, its work is more fascinating than ever.

For graduates, the opportunities are limitless. The firm fields a 22,000-strong global team of consultants, data scientists, engineers, and subject-matter experts to partner with clients on projects that make positive change happen. BCG helps organisations thrive in a world where sustainability is the priority.

Working at BCG, graduates will make an impact from day one, with early exposure to the most senior leaders of global corporations. There are opportunities to build experience across different industries and sectors, and to work in projects at the forefront of technology, like advanced robotics, artificial intelligence, and blockchain. In addition, BCG has enabled over £2bn in social impact consulting and has made its own pledge to become net zero by 2030.

This focus on the future means that BCG offers unparalleled opportunities for growth and development. The firm never stops learning: it continually invests in its employees with in-depth learning experiences, curated and led by senior BCGers and top-tier trainers from around the world.

Diversity of thought, expertise, experience, and background are fundamental to BCG's success. They are looking for bright students from any subject matter or discipline, and value people with high academic achievement, who can demonstrate leadership skills, deep intellectual curiosity, and a problem-solving mindset.

For graduates looking to continue their learning journey and make a real difference in the world, BCG is the place to start.

GRADUATE VACANCIES IN 2022
CONSULTING

NUMBER OF VACANCIES
150+ graduate jobs

LOCATIONS OF VACANCIES

STARTING SALARY FOR 2022
£Competitive

Plus a competitive compensation and benefits package, including an annual, discretionary performance-related bonus.

WORK EXPERIENCE
DEGREE PLACEMENTS

UNIVERSITY PROMOTIONS DURING 2021-2022
BATH, BIRMINGHAM, BRISTOL, CAMBRIDGE, DURHAM, EDINBURGH, EXETER, GLASGOW, IMPERIAL COLLEGE LONDON, KING'S COLLEGE LONDON, LEEDS, LIVERPOOL, LONDON SCHOOL OF ECONOMICS, MANCHESTER, NEWCASTLE, NOTTINGHAM, OXFORD, SCHOOL OF AFRICAN STUDIES, SHEFFIELD, SOUTHAMPTON, ST ANDREWS, UNIVERSITY COLLEGE LONDON, WARWICK, YORK

Please check with your university careers service for full details of BCG's local promotions and events.

MINIMUM ENTRY REQUIREMENTS
2.1 Degree

APPLICATION DEADLINE
28th October 2021

FURTHER INFORMATION
www.Top100GraduateEmployers.com

Register now for the latest news, local promotions, work experience and graduate vacancies at BCG.

Design the Future.
Welcome to the Group.

careers.bcg.com

Beyond consultants and business strategists, we are a network of data scientists, user experience designers, and experts across every field, industry, and region. We go beyond ideas to find solutions and put them into meaningful action. By helping our clients do amazing things, we help change the world.

bp

bp delivers heat, light, and mobility products and services to customers around the world, and is doing so in ways that are helping drive the transition to a lower carbon future. The business employs over 63,600 people in operations in Europe, North and South America, Australasia, Asia, and Africa.

bp's purpose is to reimagine energy for people and the planet. To achieve this, bp is transforming its entire business. It's investing to grow renewable energy, expanding charging to support the growth of electric vehicles, and focusing its oil and gas business worldwide on higher quality and lower carbon operations.

This purpose is a driving force in bp, and it's shared by a global team. From engineers and scientists to traders and data analysts, they work together to drive the energy transformation. The professionals on bp's early talent programmes make an important contribution. Whether they are in business, digital, engineering, science, or trading, they bring their own ideas, ambitions, and perspectives to the table.

bp's internship and graduate programmes give new joiners a platform to achieve their full potential. Paid 11-week and year-long internships offer hands-on business experience to undergraduates or postgraduates who are about to start the final year of their degree or PhD. Graduates on their two- or three-year programmes gain a full range of skills and experience. And each programme is designed to open up a variety of opportunities and roles across bp.

Diverse and inclusive, bp's culture focuses on teamwork, respect, and ambition. Right from the start, students are offered a real chance to build a challenging, varied career and to contribute at any stage of the energy lifecycle. The result is a positive, supportive environment where everyone can achieve their ambitions while making a meaningful impact that reaches far beyond the business.

GRADUATE VACANCIES IN 2022

ENGINEERING
FINANCE
HUMAN RESOURCES
LOGISTICS
MARKETING
PURCHASING
RESEARCH & DEVELOPMENT
SALES
TECHNOLOGY

NUMBER OF VACANCIES
100+ graduate jobs

LOCATIONS OF VACANCIES

STARTING SALARY FOR 2022
£35,000
Plus a £3,000 settling-in allowance.

UNIVERSITY PROMOTIONS DURING 2021-2022
ABERDEEN, ASTON, BATH, BELFAST, BIRMINGHAM, CAMBRIDGE, DURHAM, HERIOT-WATT, IMPERIAL COLLEGE LONDON, LANCASTER, LEEDS, LEICESTER, LIVERPOOL, LONDON SCHOOL OF ECONOMICS, LOUGHBOROUGH, MANCHESTER, NEWCASTLE, NOTTINGHAM, OXFORD, SHEFFIELD, SOUTHAMPTON, STRATHCLYDE, SURREY, UNIVERSITY COLLEGE LONDON
Please check with your university careers service for full details of bp's local promotions and events.

MINIMUM ENTRY REQUIREMENTS
2.1 Degree

APPLICATION DEADLINE
Varies by function

FURTHER INFORMATION
www.Top100GraduateEmployers.com
Register now for the latest news, local promotions, work experience and graduate vacancies at bp.

Be part of reimagining *energy*

Intern and graduate opportunities in
Business | Digital | Engineering | Science | Trading

bp

There's a lot to be part of at bp. We're reimagining energy and transforming our business – reducing our emissions, growing our low-carbon energy businesses, and forming partnerships around the world. Join us and you'll share this progress. You'll drive it too. Working with colleagues worldwide, you'll deliver projects that really matter and make an impact that reaches far beyond bp. To hear from some of the people behind our progress, follow us on social media. Or visit our careers site to see our opportunities and find out where you could fit in.

bp.com/grads/uk

- @ life.at.bp
- @ bp_plc
- @ bpcareers
- @ bp

Every day, BT touches millions of people's lives. The NHS, emergency services, contactless payments – they all operate thanks to BT's services, technology, and innovations. BT is a people-led business, committed to continually creating imaginative new products that help keep the nation running.

As a global company operating in over 180 countries, BT isn't just a UK broadband provider: it's at the forefront of the latest technology developments worldwide. Thanks to its size and reach, BT is able to encourage and empower its graduate community – to let them get stuck in from day one, pitch in with ideas, and make things happen.

Despite the way people work being subject to huge changes at the moment, BT remains brilliantly placed to kick-start graduate careers. With 100,000 employees globally, it's able to ensure graduates can adapt, learn, and re-invent themselves, and continue to grow in the workplace. It's one company where the young talent of today won't outgrow the roles of the future.

It's also as ambitious as its graduates are. BT aims to improve the digital skills of ten million people in this country by 2025; it strives to keep people secure online while protecting privacy and free expression; and it's adopting a sector-leading approach to climate action – aiming to be carbon-neutral by 2045.

BT has a huge range of opportunities for graduates in every part of its business. Whatever their area of interest in the industry may be, graduates will find a role that's exciting, challenging, and unexpected. As a company that embraces diversity and inclusion, new joiners will be warmly welcomed, whatever their background. And it offers the promise of a career in an organisation that continually strives to make a difference.

Hoping for more than just a job? Take a look at what BT can offer.

GRADUATE VACANCIES IN 2022
FINANCE
GENERAL MANAGEMENT
HUMAN RESOURCES
MARKETING
RESEARCH & DEVELOPMENT
SALES
TECHNOLOGY

NUMBER OF VACANCIES
200-250 graduate jobs

LOCATIONS OF VACANCIES

STARTING SALARY FOR 2022
£29,100-£30,500
Plus a 10% on-target bonus.

WORK EXPERIENCE
DEGREE PLACEMENTS   SUMMER INTERNSHIPS

UNIVERSITY PROMOTIONS DURING 2021-2022
BELFAST, BIRMINGHAM, CARDIFF, MANCHESTER, NOTTINGHAM TRENT, QUEEN MARY LONDON, UEA
Please check with your university careers service for full details of BT's local promotions and events.

MINIMUM ENTRY REQUIREMENTS
2.1 Degree

APPLICATION DEADLINE
Year-round recruitment
Early application is advised.

FURTHER INFORMATION
www.Top100GraduateEmployers.com
Register now for the latest news, local promotions, work experience and graduate vacancies at BT.

It's good to want more.

That's how we think at BT. We like to say that we 'connect for good'; when we do, businesses grow, communities flourish and people get more out of life. But we want even more than that.

We want BT to be a place where our people are inspired to be the best they can be. Where we celebrate diversity, and new ideas drive us forward.

We need brilliant people who share our ambition to make that happen. Join us, and every day you'll have the chance to challenge yourself – intellectually and creatively.

Innovation is part of who we are. We're at the heart of the 5G revolution, which is changing technology as we know it. We're using the Internet of Things to help develop smart cities, improving their efficiency and the wellbeing of their citizens. And we're part of a project that will set a new global standard for green recovery and sustainability. We want you to help us stay at the cutting edge.

And we'll never stop encouraging you to fulfil your potential. On our graduate programme, you'll be in a real role, with real responsibility, from day one. But you'll also have access to coaching, networking and knowledge-sharing – and you'll have a mentor and a buddy to support you all the way.

We go out of our way to offer all our employees a range of benefits that reflect the full value of their skills, experience and qualifications. And if it's right for our business and our customers, we'll support you in working flexibly, too.

It's crucial for our people to reflect the diversity of our customers, in this country and around the world. And we know that having people from all walks of life makes us a stronger and more innovative company.

We've opportunities for graduates across the whole of our business – so whatever your area of interest, if you want more from a career, you'll find it at BT. We're constantly striving to learn and grow, and with your help – together – we can.

BT.com/graduates

GRADUATE VACANCIES IN 2022

ACCOUNTANCY
CONSULTING
FINANCE
GENERAL MANAGEMENT
HUMAN RESOURCES
MARKETING
RESEARCH & DEVELOPMENT

NUMBER OF VACANCIES
100 graduate jobs

LOCATIONS OF VACANCIES

STARTING SALARY FOR 2022
£18,800-£21,600

UNIVERSITY PROMOTIONS DURING 2021-2022
ABERDEEN, ASTON, BATH, BIRMINGHAM, BRISTOL, BRUNEL, CAMBRIDGE, CARDIFF, DURHAM, EDINBURGH, ESSEX, EXETER, GLASGOW, IMPERIAL COLLEGE LONDON, KING'S COLLEGE LONDON, KENT, LANCASTER, LEEDS, LEICESTER, LIVERPOOL, LONDON SCHOOL OF ECONOMICS, LOUGHBOROUGH, MANCHESTER, NEWCASTLE, NORTHUMBRIA, NOTTINGHAM, NOTTINGHAM TRENT, OXFORD, OXFORD BROOKES, QUEEN MARY LONDON, READING, ROYAL HOLLOWAY, SCHOOL OF AFRICAN STUDIES, SHEFFIELD, SOUTHAMPTON, SURREY, SUSSEX, SWANSEA, UEA, UNIVERSITY COLLEGE LONDON, WARWICK, YORK
Please check with your university careers service for full details of Charityworks' local promotions and events.

APPLICATION DEADLINE
February 2022

FURTHER INFORMATION
www.Top100GraduateEmployers.com
*Register now for the latest news, local promotions, work experience and graduate vacancies at **Charityworks**.*

Charityworks is the graduate programme for the UK non-profit sector, placing over 100 graduates each year. The programme comprises a 12-month full-time placement with one of their partner charities or housing associations, combined with an acclaimed leadership development programme.

In their placement, Charityworks trainees could be providing vital business support at a national charity like NSPCC, leading on infrastructure projects with a housing charity, or serving a community in a local project. Wherever they are placed, trainees will have the chance to make a real impact through their work.

Alongside the placement, trainees take part in an ILM-endorsed leadership development programme. They are supported by the Charityworks programme team and an external mentor to help them to make the most of the experience. Throughout the year, trainees join together with their cohort and leaders across the sector to explore the key issues affecting their work and society as a whole. They also produce their own research, helping to raise their profile and develop their understanding of the charity sector environment.

At the end of the 12-month scheme, trainees have the experience and skills to kickstart their professional careers in the UK social sector and beyond. Charityworks graduates are highly desired, with 98% securing employment within 3 months. Typically, over 66% of graduates stay in their host organisations at the end of the year, and 96% of graduates since 2009 have remained within the non-profit or public sector – some have even gone on to start their own organisations!

Whatever graduates want to do in the long-term, Charityworks is a great way to launch their career and get paid to change the world.

POVERTY.
AFFORDABLE HOUSING.
DOMESTIC VIOLENCE.
CLIMATE CHANGE.
SOCIAL CARE.

WHAT ROLE WILL YOU PLAY?

Charityworks.
Change the world
for a living.

careers that make a difference

Civil Service
Fast Stream

GRADUATE VACANCIES IN 2022

ENGINEERING

FINANCE

GENERAL MANAGEMENT

HUMAN RESOURCES

PROPERTY

PURCHASING

RESEARCH & DEVELOPMENT

TECHNOLOGY

NUMBER OF VACANCIES
950 graduate jobs

LOCATIONS OF VACANCIES

The Civil Service supports the government of the day to implement its policies effectively on behalf of every community across the UK. The award-winning Fast Stream leadership programme develops talented, high-potential graduates from all backgrounds to become the future leaders of the Civil Service.

Fast Streamers help to deliver vital public services and shape the decisions that affect everyone's lives. The Fast Stream offers proactive and open-minded graduates a choice of 15 different schemes, designed to accelerate their progression to the most senior Civil Service roles. Each scheme provides a high-quality structured learning programme and a career development path within a government profession.

Regardless of the degree subject they studied, graduates will be able to find a scheme that's right for them. Different schemes provide options to fit a range of circumstances. Most provide a series of postings with different government departments at rotating locations across the UK. Several offer the opportunity to study for a professional qualification.

Supported by a range of professionals whose priority is creating the right conditions for growth and success, graduates develop their skills, knowledge, and experience across a broad span of work. They are given early responsibility and empowered to turn their ideas into action.

Fast Streamers are valued members of the wider Civil Service community, where people of all ages, cultures, and backgrounds can form lasting friendships and support one another on their development journeys. In addition, flexible working arrangements offer the space to achieve work-life balance, while a variety of Fast Stream experiences provide the opportunity to build a range of valuable networks around work.

STARTING SALARY FOR 2022
£28,000

WORK EXPERIENCE
SUMMER
INTERNSHIPS

UNIVERSITY PROMOTIONS DURING 2021-2022
Please check with your university careers service for full details of the Civil Service's local promotions and events.

MINIMUM ENTRY REQUIREMENT
2.2 Degree

APPLICATION DEADLINE
Late October 2021

FURTHER INFORMATION
www.Top100GraduateEmployers.com
Register now for the latest news, local promotions, work experience and graduate vacancies at the Civil Service.

Civil Service
Fast Stream

FROM health legislation to environmental policy TO JUSTICE REFORM

Graduate Leadership Development Programme
In Yasmin's first year with us, she worked on the Coronavirus Act. Now she's on secondment
with a women's charity, growing new skills in an area that means a lot to her. And after that?
It could be Defra or the Ministry of Justice. Wherever she goes on the Fast Stream, Yasmin takes
every opportunity to realise her potential. You can too. The Civil Service touches all aspects
of UK life. So, with a range of 15 different leadership and specialist development schemes
to choose from, you'll find there's something here for you – whatever your degree subject,
background or age. **Explore more at faststream.gov.uk**

You, unlimited.

CMS is a future facing firm. Whether stakeholders are big or small, they always have the firm's full attention and expertise. In a world of ever-accelerating change – where technology is increasingly important – their clear, business-focused advice helps clients of every size to face the future with confidence.

CMS is a full-service law firm combining top quality sector expertise with international scale. They embrace technology and are committed to new ideas that challenge conventional ways of doing things. CMS puts the interests of clients at the heart of everything they do across 70+ offices in 40+ countries in the UK, Europe, the Middle East, Africa, Asia, and South America. With more than 1,100 partners and 5,000 lawyers, CMS works in cross-border teams to deliver top quality, practical advice. The firm is recognised for its sector excellence and focus in consumer products; energy; financial institutions; hotels & leisure; infrastructure & projects; life sciences & healthcare; real estate; and technology, media & telecommunications.

When it comes to what they're looking for, keen intellect is vital, but CMS are looking for much more than academic qualifications. Whether applicants are law students, non-law students or career changers, the skills required include personal effectiveness, professional communication, drive for achievement, and having a future facing outlook.

The main route to a training contract at CMS is by successfully completing the CMS Academy programme. Their two-year training contracts feature four six-month seats or national, international, or client secondments. CMS also offers insight to the firm through their First Steps programme, apprenticeships, widening participation work experience and scholarship opportunities, and the newly launched Business Development & Marketing Graduate Programme.

GRADUATE VACANCIES IN 2022
LAW
MARKETING

NUMBER OF VACANCIES
79+ graduate jobs
For training contracts starting in 2024.

LOCATIONS OF VACANCIES

Vacancies also available in Europe, Asia, and elsewhere in the world.

STARTING SALARY FOR 2022
£25,500-£44,500

WORK EXPERIENCE
INSIGHT COURSES | SUMMER INTERNSHIPS

UNIVERSITY PROMOTIONS DURING 2021-2022
ABERDEEN, BIRMINGHAM, BRISTOL, CAMBRIDGE, CARDIFF, DUNDEE, DURHAM, EDINBURGH, EXETER, GLASGOW, KING'S COLLEGE LONDON, KENT, LANCASTER, LEEDS, LEICESTER, LIVERPOOL, LONDON SCHOOL OF ECONOMICS, MANCHESTER, NEWCASTLE, NOTTINGHAM, NOTTINGHAM TRENT, OXFORD, QUEEN MARY LONDON, SHEFFIELD, SOUTHAMPTON, UEA, UNIVERSITY COLLEGE LONDON, WARWICK, YORK
Please check with your university careers service for full details of CMS's local promotions and events.

APPLICATION DEADLINE
Varies by function

FURTHER INFORMATION
www.Top100GraduateEmployers.com
Register now for the latest news, local promotions, work experience and graduate vacancies at CMS.

Deloitte makes its impact through collaboration. All around the world, their colleagues spark positive progress for their clients, people and society. Their curiosity creates all kinds of possibilities in the worlds of business and technology. There's a purpose here to believe in, and an impact that everyone can see.

From Human Capital, Tax Consulting, and Legal to Technology and Cyber, Deloitte is delivering end-to-end improvement programmes. They're turning disruption into opportunity, and redesigning Audit through automation. To do this, they're drawing on the strengths and perspectives of everyone in the business – including their graduates.

At Deloitte, graduates are supported to make a serious contribution to the projects and the business, in an environment where they can be their true selves, dream bigger, think creatively, and deliver real impact. And they can progress and learn every day – from the work they do, and the people they collaborate with.

It's not the background of graduates that matters here. It's their questioning minds, determination to make a difference, and eagerness to work with others to solve problems. These are the qualities that are embraced and developed at Deloitte. And with countless opportunities in different business areas, industries, and sectors, graduates will always find challenges that motivate and inspire them.

Deloitte has offices across the UK and Northern Ireland, including Aberdeen, Belfast, Cardiff, Channel Islands, London, Manchester, Reading, and many more. Wherever they join, graduates can be sure of joining a local and global business, with networks, connections, and shared values that reach right across the world.

Graduates at Deloitte can experience more, and go further. Join them, and create your own path.

GRADUATE VACANCIES IN 2022

ACCOUNTANCY
CONSULTING
FINANCE
HUMAN RESOURCES
LAW
PROPERTY
TECHNOLOGY

NUMBER OF VACANCIES
1,000+ graduate jobs

LOCATIONS OF VACANCIES

STARTING SALARY FOR 2022
£Competitive

WORK EXPERIENCE

| INSIGHT COURSES | DEGREE PLACEMENTS | SUMMER INTERNSHIPS |

UNIVERSITY PROMOTIONS DURING 2021-2022
Please check with your university careers service for full details of Deloitte's local promotions and events.

MINIMUM ENTRY REQUIREMENTS
2.1 Degree, 104 UCAS points
260 UCAS points for those who passed exams before 2017.

APPLICATION DEADLINE
Varies by function

FURTHER INFORMATION
www.Top100GraduateEmployers.com
Register now for the latest news, local promotions, work experience and graduate vacancies at Deloitte.

Deloitte.

Share our purpose.
Create your own path.

Choosing Deloitte means choosing opportunity.
The diversity of our business and the industries
we work in will offer you countless ways to
progress, contribute and shine. And whichever
path you take, we'll be right there with you.

What impact will you make?
deloitte.co.uk/careers

GRADUATE VACANCIES IN 2022

FINANCE

INVESTMENT BANKING

TECHNOLOGY

NUMBER OF VACANCIES
100+ graduate jobs

LOCATIONS OF VACANCIES

Vacancies also available in Europe, the USA, and Asia.

STARTING SALARY FOR 2022
£Competitive
Plus a competitive bonus.

WORK EXPERIENCE

DEGREE PLACEMENTS   SUMMER INTERNSHIPS

UNIVERSITY PROMOTIONS DURING 2021-2022
ASTON, BATH, BIRMINGHAM, BRISTOL, CAMBRIDGE, CARDIFF, CITY, DURHAM, EDINBURGH, ESSEX, EXETER, GLASGOW, IMPERIAL COLLEGE LONDON, KING'S COLLEGE LONDON, LANCASTER, LEEDS, LEICESTER, LONDON SCHOOL OF ECONOMICS, LOUGHBOROUGH, MANCHESTER, NEWCASTLE, NOTTINGHAM, OXFORD, QUEEN MARY LONDON, SOUTHAMPTON, ST ANDREWS, SURREY, UNIVERSITY COLLEGE LONDON, WARWICK, YORK
Please check with your university careers service for full details of Deutsche Bank's local promotions and events.

MINIMUM ENTRY REQUIREMENTS
2.1 Degree

APPLICATION DEADLINE
Varies by function

FURTHER INFORMATION
www.Top100GraduateEmployers.com
Register now for the latest news, local promotions, work experience and graduate vacancies at Deutsche Bank.

Deutsche Bank is the leading German bank, with strong European roots and a global network. It delivers banking services to corporations, governments, and private individuals around the world, enabling economic growth and societal progress for their clients, people, investors, and communities.

As an established organisation with a global footprint, Deutsche Bank leads the finance industry into the future by making cutting-edge technology its centre of strategy going forwards. It creates solutions to the industry's biggest challenges and is looking for creative and curious graduates ready to make a difference today.

Deutsche Bank's early careers programmes offer students and graduates the opportunity to shape their own career, as well as the future of the financial industry. Its global platform and world-class training opportunities provide essential skills through smart learning, tailored development, and working on exciting projects alongside the brightest minds in the industry.

There are multiple ways to start a career with Deutsche Bank: from insight days, spring weeks, and internships to full-time graduate roles across a variety of business divisions. Students and graduates are always given the time and support to make a real difference on real projects, while finding the area that most excites them.

Deutsche Bank is proud to be an equal opportunity employer and is committed to creating a culture of belonging, diversity, and inclusion that helps anyone with the necessary talent and drive to succeed. It looks for individuals with an eye for detail, a view towards the big picture, and an interest in challenging the status quo. Joining Deutsche Bank means joining an organisation dedicated to delivering innovation and creating a positive impact from day one.

DIAGEO

From Arthur Guinness to Johnnie Walker, Diageo was founded on people of character. Graduates help to bring that character so Diageo can remain the world's leading premium alcohol company. Graduates are trusted with the company's legacy and rewarded with career-defining opportunities.

At Diageo, character is everything. The international team spans more than 180 countries and multiple brands to create 26 billion drinks every single year. From Smirnoff and Tanqueray to Guinness and Johnnie Walker, the business is enhanced by a dynamic community of individuals who are passionate about their work. And when graduates join Diageo, they will be right at the heart of that work.

When graduates bring their best to the Diageo Graduate Programme, they will go further than they ever thought possible. The Graduate Programme is a two- or three-year adventure in one of five business areas: Marketing, Sales, Human Resources, Finance, or Supply. Wherever graduates start, they will be challenged and inspired to reach their full potential.

Graduates develop knowledge in a chosen scheme area and high-quality leadership skills. This will happen through a combination of formal training, mentoring, and coaching from respected colleagues and, most importantly, real world, on-the-job experience. Working with a diverse and vibrant workforce in an inclusive environment will help graduates to perform at their best every step of the way. From the start, graduates work on projects that challenge them and put their skills to the test. Graduates are able to make a real contribution to the business while building a global network of relationships that support careers, both now and long into the future.

To find out more about this unique opportunity, visit the Diageo careers site.

GRADUATE VACANCIES IN 2022
ENGINEERING
FINANCE
HUMAN RESOURCES
LOGISTICS
MARKETING
RESEARCH & DEVELOPMENT
SALES

NUMBER OF VACANCIES
70 graduate jobs

LOCATIONS OF VACANCIES

Vacancies also available in Europe.

STARTING SALARY FOR 2022
£36,400
Plus an annual bonus incentive plan.

UNIVERSITY PROMOTIONS DURING 2021-2022
ASTON, BATH, BIRMINGHAM, BRISTOL, BRUNEL, EDINBURGH, GLASGOW, HERIOT-WATT, IMPERIAL COLLEGE LONDON, KING'S COLLEGE LONDON, LEEDS, LONDON SCHOOL OF ECONOMICS, MANCHESTER, NOTTINGHAM, OXFORD, QMUL, SHEFFIELD, ST ANDREWS, STRATHCLYDE, ULSTER, UCL
Please check with your university careers service for full details of Diageo's local promotions and events.

MINIMUM ENTRY REQUIREMENTS
Varies by function
Relevant degree required for some roles.

APPLICATION DEADLINE
Varies by function

FURTHER INFORMATION
www.Top100GraduateEmployers.com
Register now for the latest news, local promotions, work experience and graduate vacancies at Diageo.

CHARACTER IS EVERYTHING

DIAGEO

GRADUATE VACANCIES IN 2022
LAW

NUMBER OF VACANCIES
60-70 graduate jobs
For training contracts starting in 2024.

LOCATIONS OF VACANCIES

Vacancies also available elsewhere in the world.

STARTING SALARY FOR 2022
£46,000
London.

£30,000
Rest of the UK.

€47,000
Dublin.

WORK EXPERIENCE
DEGREE PLACEMENTS | SUMMER INTERNSHIPS

UNIVERSITY PROMOTIONS DURING 2021-2022
ABERDEEN, BIRMINGHAM, BRISTOL, CAMBRIDGE, DUNDEE, EDINBURGH, EXETER, GLASGOW, KING'S COLLEGE LONDON, LEEDS, LEICESTER, LIVERPOOL, LONDON SCHOOL OF ECONOMICS, MANCHESTER, NEWCASTLE, NOTTINGHAM, OXFORD, SHEFFIELD, ST ANDREWS, UNIVERSITY COLLEGE LONDON, WARWICK, YORK
Please check with your university careers service for full details of DLA Piper's local promotions and events.

APPLICATION DEADLINE
31st December 2021

FURTHER INFORMATION
www.Top100GraduateEmployers.com
Register now for the latest news, local promotions, work experience and graduate vacancies at DLA Piper.

DLA Piper is one of the world's leading business law firms. With over 90 offices in more than 40 countries, the firm provides seamless local and cross-border advice. The firm believes great businesses can make a better world. That's why, every day, DLA Piper helps its clients succeed.

DLA Piper's progressive mindset challenges conventions and evolves its global legal offering into broader advisory services and new business areas. Through the firm's deep industry knowledge, technological solutions, and diversity of thought and experience, clients embrace change and seize opportunities.

DLA Piper's ten sector groups cover the full range of business law services. Clients include multinationals, start-ups, public sector bodies, and governments. Across the two leading legal directories, the firm has over 3,567 lawyer rankings, and over 1,440 practice group/sector rankings. DLA Piper has a world-leading global pro bono practice, with lawyers working across Asia Pacific, Africa, the Middle East, Europe, and North America. In 2020, the firm contributed 227,508 hours of pro bono legal services globally. Internationally, the firm focus on displaced people. Their practice is uniquely placed to work to protect the rights of refugees, displaced people, and those who are stateless, with a particular focus on supporting the most vulnerable groups, including women, children, and members of the LGBT+ community.

The firms' entrepreneurial and supportive culture promotes bold, ambitious thinking and a warm, empathetic approach. Trusting, collaborative relationships with clients and each other are at the heart of everything it does. DLA Piper is looking for ambitious, capable, and forward-thinking graduates from any degree discipline to join its journey. The firm hires graduates internationally across 14 offices in Australia, Hong Kong, Ireland, UAE, and the UK.

SHARE OUR VISION
SHAPE YOUR FUTURE

Our goal is simple. We want to create the future leaders of the firm. That means giving you the skills you need to become a successful lawyer, but also the experiences to discover where your true interests lie.

Find out more at
DLAPIPERGRADUATES.COM

careers.enterprise.co.uk

facebook.com/EnterpriseRentACarJobsEurope

linkedin.com/company/enterprise-rent-a-car twitter.com/ERAC_Jobs

instagram.com/EnterpriseRentACar_Careers youtube.com/EnterpriseRentACarJobsandCareersEMEA

Enterprise started life as a small business. Still family-owned, it's grown to be the largest global mobility provider in the world, with 9,500+ branches globally, an annual turnover of $22.5 billion, and the biggest rental vehicle fleet on the planet. Join them and be one of the people driving this success.

From their senior leaders to their apprentices, Enterprise gives everyone the freedom to explore their potential and the opportunities they need to rise to new challenges and take their skills to the next level – because their growth is what makes Enterprise's growth possible.

Nowhere is this philosophy better illustrated than in their approach to graduate careers. When people join their award-winning Management Training Programme, they empower graduates to start contributing right from the word go. It helps that Enterprise are divided up into smaller, local branches, so their graduates gain the skills and experience needed to run their own business in as little as two years.

As a *Times Top 50 Employer for Women* for 16 consecutive years, Enterprise has created a work environment where women thrive and are encouraged to rise to new levels in their career, thanks to the support of both management and their peers.

Enterprise is also still family-owned – their CEO Chrissy Taylor is the third generation of the Taylor family to run the company. This allows them to look forward even more confidently to the future, providing the stability they need to pursue the long-term good for their customers, their business, and their employees, even in these challenging times.

Join Enterprise on their graduate programme and become one of the new generation helping them write the next chapter of their success story.

GRADUATE VACANCIES IN 2022
GENERAL MANAGEMENT
RETAIL
SALES

NUMBER OF VACANCIES
800+ graduate jobs

LOCATIONS OF VACANCIES

STARTING SALARY FOR 2022
£22,000
Plus performance-based bonuses once the graduate programme has been completed, and location allowance if applicable.

WORK EXPERIENCE
| DEGREE PLACEMENTS | SUMMER INTERNSHIPS |

UNIVERSITY PROMOTIONS DURING 2021-2022
ABERDEEN, ABERYSTWYTH, ASTON, BELFAST, BIRMINGHAM, BRADFORD, BRISTOL, BRUNEL, CARDIFF, CITY, DUNDEE, ESSEX, EXETER, GLASGOW, HERIOT-WATT, HULL, KENT, LEEDS, LEICESTER, LIVERPOOL, LOUGHBOROUGH, MANCHESTER, NEWCASTLE, NORTHUMBRIA, NOTTINGHAM, NOTTINGHAM TRENT, OXFORD BROOKES, PLYMOUTH, QMUL, READING, ROYAL HOLLOWAY, SHEFFIELD, SOUTHAMPTON, STIRLING, STRATHCLYDE, SURREY, SUSSEX, SWANSEA, UEA, ULSTER, YORK

MINIMUM ENTRY REQUIREMENTS
Any degree accepted

APPLICATION DEADLINE
Year-round recruitment
Early application is advised.

FURTHER INFORMATION
www.Top100GraduateEmployers.com
Register now for the latest news, local promotions, work experience and graduate vacancies at Enterprise.

Your prospects

Do wonders for them as an
Intern or **Management Trainee**

What does a graduate career with the
world's largest car rental company look
like? It starts in one of our 9,500 branches
worldwide. It continues with you becoming a
manager of one of those branches, in as little
as two years' time. From there, you can go
in whatever direction you choose. National
sales? Business rental? Human resources?
The choice is yours. And whether you join us
on our award-winning Management Trainee
programme or as an Intern, you'll enjoy
great benefits, excellent training and
real responsibility from day one.

Discover more at
careers.enterprise.co.uk

enterprise

EY
Building a better
working world

EY is one of the world's most influential professional services organisations. Operating across 150 countries with over 700 office locations, EY acts as a trusted partner to its clients, drawing upon fresh thinking and advanced technology to help make better business decisions.

With a clear purpose of building a better working world, EY believes that, by asking better questions, it can find better answers to some of today's most pressing issues. How can teams futureproof businesses? How will EY keep client data secure in a digital world filled with risk? How can EY colleagues take organisations to the next level in order to compete in the future? These are just a few of the questions that students could be tackling on one of EY's undergraduate or graduate programmes.

EY is home to some 300,000 people, who are each diverse and unique, with a breadth of passions and interests. What unites them is their curiosity. They find a sense of belonging at EY – not only because of its open and inclusive culture, but because everyone welcomes diverse perspectives and unique voices.

Whichever business area undergraduates and graduates join – Assurance, Consulting, Strategy and Transactions, or Tax – there's real scope for impact. Ideas will be welcomed and, across everything, they could harness the potential of pioneering technologies like artificial intelligence, machine learning, or robotic process automation. And with continued flexible working, they can work in EY's world, their way.

Students will have all the scope and autonomy needed to erase industry boundaries, to innovate, evolve, and thrive as they hone their skills on a broad range of local and global projects. This is an opportunity for them to be themselves, and become everything they ever wanted to be.

GRADUATE VACANCIES IN 2022

ACCOUNTANCY

CONSULTING

FINANCE

TECHNOLOGY

NUMBER OF VACANCIES
950+ graduate jobs

LOCATIONS OF VACANCIES

STARTING SALARY FOR 2022
£Competitive

WORK EXPERIENCE

| INSIGHT COURSES | DEGREE PLACEMENTS | SUMMER INTERNSHIPS |

UNIVERSITY PROMOTIONS DURING 2021-2022
ABERDEEN, ASTON, BATH, BELFAST, BIRMINGHAM, BRISTOL, BRUNEL, CAMBRIDGE, DURHAM, EDINBURGH, ESSEX, EXETER, GLASGOW, HERIOT-WATT, HULL, IMPERIAL COLLEGE LONDON, KING'S COLLEGE LONDON, KENT, LANCASTER, LEEDS, LEICESTER, LIVERPOOL, LSE, LOUGHBOROUGH, MANCHESTER, NEWCASTLE, NOTTINGHAM, NOTTINGHAM TRENT, QMUL, READING, ROYAL HOLLOWAY, SHEFFIELD, SOUTHAMPTON, ST ANDREWS, STRATHCLYDE, SURREY, UCL, WARWICK, YORK

MINIMUM ENTRY REQUIREMENTS
Varies by function
Relevant degree required for some roles.

APPLICATION DEADLINE
Year-round recruitment
Early application is advised.

FURTHER INFORMATION
www.Top100GraduateEmployers.com
Register now for the latest news, local promotions, work experience and graduate vacancies at EY.

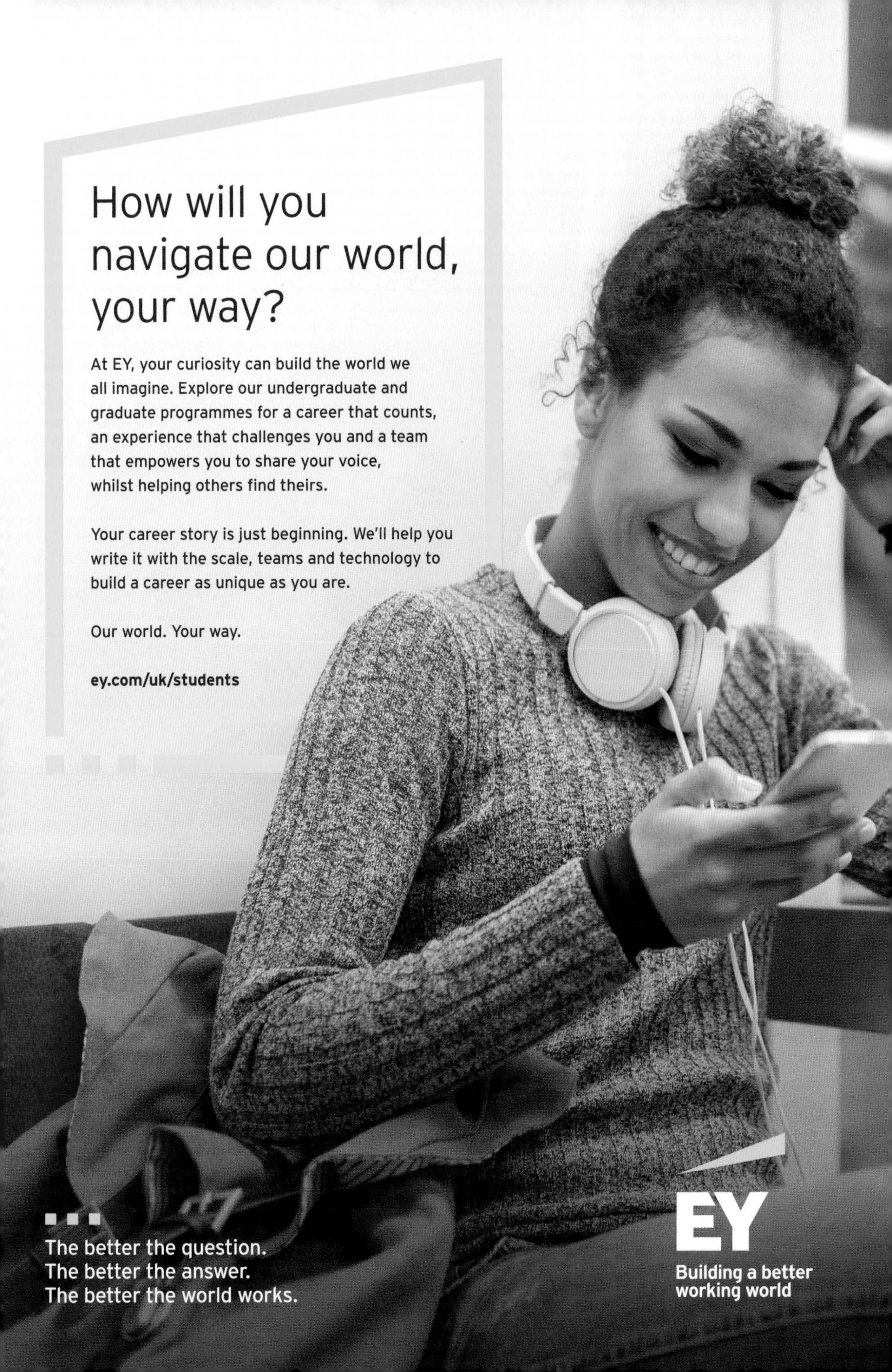

How will you navigate our world, your way?

At EY, your curiosity can build the world we all imagine. Explore our undergraduate and graduate programmes for a career that counts, an experience that challenges you and a team that empowers you to share your voice, whilst helping others find theirs.

Your career story is just beginning. We'll help you write it with the scale, teams and technology to build a career as unique as you are.

Our world. Your way.

ey.com/uk/students

The better the question.
The better the answer.
The better the world works.

EY
Building a better
working world

Freshfields is one of the world's oldest and most successful international law firms. As such, the firm has a long-standing track record of successfully supporting the world's leading national and multinational corporations, financial institutions, and governments on their business-critical mandates.

Whether it's entering new markets, defending corporate reputation, or managing multijurisdictional regulation, Freshfields is renowned for breaking new legal ground to help clients go further.

Freshfields lawyers deliver results worldwide through their own offices in the world's main business centres. They also work alongside leading local firms and, as a result, more than a third of their revenue comes from markets where Freshfields doesn't have a permanent presence. Freshfields provides local and multinational expertise so its clients can make the right decisions in a rapidly changing world.

Freshfields' people make the firm. Freshfields looks for people who think globally and are at their best when working with others. It looks for graduates who are creative, open-minded and curious about different ways of doing things, because it's not only understanding the law which is important, but each client's own business, the sector in which it operates, and the broader economic, political, and cultural factors that affect its decisions.

Freshfields commits to its values, including treating everyone with respect, consideration, and courtesy, and working together to deliver exceptional service. It is committed to being a responsible, diverse and inclusive business.

The firm's unique eight-seat training contract lays the foundation for a career at the cutting edge of corporate law and the opportunity to develop – not just as a lawyer, but as a person, too.

GRADUATE VACANCIES IN 2022
LAW

NUMBER OF VACANCIES
Up to 80 graduate jobs
For training contracts starting in 2024.

LOCATIONS OF VACANCIES

Vacancies also available in Asia.

STARTING SALARY FOR 2022
£45,000
In first year.
Increasing to £51,000 in second year.

WORK EXPERIENCE
INSIGHT COURSES | SUMMER INTERNSHIPS

UNIVERSITY PROMOTIONS DURING 2021-2022
Please check with your university careers service for full details of Freshfields' local promotions and events.

APPLICATION DEADLINE
6th January 2022

FURTHER INFORMATION
www.Top100GraduateEmployers.com
Register now for the latest news, local promotions, work experience and graduate vacancies at Freshfields.

Expect more_

Go further with Freshfields

Apply now
ukgraduates.freshfields.com

 Freshfields

FRONTLINE
CHANGING LIVES

thefrontline.org.uk

facebook.com/FrontlineChangingLives
recruitment@thefrontline.org.uk
linkedin.com/company/frontline-org
twitter.com/FrontlineSW
instagram.com/Frontline_SW
youtube.com/FrontlineChangingLives

Imagine a world where no child's life chances are limited by their social or family circumstance. That's the future Frontline is working towards. Frontline is a social work charity working to create social change for children in England without a safe or stable home, and for their families.

Over 700,000 children in England rely on the support of social workers each year. These children need and deserve the support of life-changing social work professionals, who can empower them to achieve their full potential and help to break the cycle of trauma and disadvantage. That's why Frontline develops excellent social work practice and leadership through their programmes and the Frontline Fellowship.

Graduates can join the two-year Frontline programme and gain skills in leadership, conflict resolution, and relationship building, with which they will bring about change inside the social work profession and beyond.

Graduates will work directly with children and families, helping them make positive changes in their lives, qualifying as a social worker, and completing a fully funded Master's degree. High-quality supervision and training from experienced social workers, academics, and coaches provide a rich, supportive environment for graduates to develop their professional skills and leadership. Graduates earn as they learn with a bursary in year one and a salary in year two.

By completing the Frontline programme, graduates join the Frontline Fellowship: a growing community of passionate individuals working inside and outside of the social work system to pursue wider social justice and amplify the voices of children and families. They will continue to be inspired and supported by the community of like-minded fellows and receive ongoing support and training from Frontline throughout their careers.

GRADUATE VACANCIES IN 2022
SOCIAL WORK

NUMBER OF VACANCIES
450+ graduate jobs

LOCATIONS OF VACANCIES

STARTING SALARY FOR 2022
£18,000-£20,000
As a tax-free bursary in year one.
Plus a fully funded Master's degree.

UNIVERSITY PROMOTIONS DURING 2021-2022
ASTON, BATH, BIRMINGHAM, BRISTOL, BRUNEL, CAMBRIDGE, CARDIFF, DURHAM, EDINBURGH, ESSEX, EXETER, KING'S COLLEGE LONDON, KENT, LANCASTER, LEEDS, LEICESTER, LIVERPOOL, LONDON SCHOOL OF ECONOMICS, LOUGHBOROUGH, MANCHESTER, NEWCASTLE, NORTHUMBRIA, NOTTINGHAM, NOTTINGHAM TRENT, OXFORD, PLYMOUTH, QUEEN MARY LONDON, READING, SHEFFIELD, SOUTHAMPTON, ST ANDREWS, SURREY, UNIVERSITY COLLEGE LONDON, WARWICK, YORK
Please check with your university careers service for full details of Frontline's local promotions and events.

MINIMUM ENTRY REQUIREMENTS
2.1 Degree

APPLICATION DEADLINE
Year-round recruitment
Early application is advised.

FURTHER INFORMATION
www.Top100GraduateEmployers.com
Register now for the latest news, local promotions, work experience and graduate vacancies at Frontline.

GRADUATE VACANCIES IN 2022
ENGINEERING
GENERAL MANAGEMENT
INTELLIGENCE GATHERING
RESEARCH & DEVELOPMENT
TECHNOLOGY

NUMBER OF VACANCIES
200+ graduate jobs

LOCATIONS OF VACANCIES

STARTING SALARY FOR 2022
£30,000+

WORK EXPERIENCE
| INSIGHT COURSES | DEGREE PLACEMENTS | SUMMER INTERNSHIPS |

UNIVERSITY PROMOTIONS DURING 2021-2022
Please check with your university careers service for full details of GCHQ's local promotions and events.

MINIMUM ENTRY REQUIREMENTS
Varies by function
Relevant degree required for some roles.

APPLICATION DEADLINE
Varies by function

FURTHER INFORMATION
www.Top100GraduateEmployers.com
Register now for the latest news, local promotions, work experience and graduate vacancies at GCHQ.

Government Communications Headquarters (GCHQ) is the UK's signals intelligence and cyber security agency. It works alongside MI5 and SIS (MI6) to keep the UK and its citizens safe at home, overseas and online. Using cutting-edge technology and technical ingenuity, GCHQ's mission is to counter threats including terrorism, espionage, organised crime, and cyber-attacks.

GCHQ is looking for graduates with different skills, backgrounds, and perspectives to help protect the UK. There are a range of graduate roles available in areas including technology, maths, language, analysis, and project management. Students can take advantage of a variety of paid summer placements in cyber, maths, and languages. Bursaries are also available to students studying any degree who have an interest in cyber security. Graduates joining GCHQ can expect challenging projects, outstanding professional development, and a rewarding career experience.

GCHQ is proud of its mission and its people. Its working culture encourages open minds and attitudes and is supported by a welfare and benefits structure that enables its workforce to be at its best. From extensive training and development that helps employees expand their skills to flexible working patterns that support a healthy work-life balance, GCHQ seeks to create an environment where everyone can achieve their full potential.

Applications are welcome from everyone, regardless of age, experience, cultural background, and sexual orientation. Due to the sensitive nature of the work, there are strict nationality, residency, and security requirements, and all applicants will be subject to a rigorous but fair vetting process. Applicants will need to be British citizens and need to have lived in the UK for seven out of the last ten years before applying, although some exceptions may apply.

WITH THE RIGHT MIX OF MINDS, ANYTHING IS POSSIBLE.

At GCHQ, we have a clear purpose - we want to help protect the UK. We work against cyber-attacks, terrorism and espionage. It's unique work that relies on people with unique perspectives. That's why we'll never ask you to be anything other than yourself. For us, having a diverse workforce isn't a box ticking exercise, it's an essential part of keeping the UK safe.

To find out more about our variety of roles, please visit **www.gchq-careers.co.uk**

@GCHQ   @GCHQ   GCHQ

2021/22 UK 300   Stonewall DIVERSITY CHAMPION   disability confident LEADER

Goldman Sachs is a leading global financial services firm providing investment banking, securities, and investment management services to a substantial and diversified client base that includes corporations, financial institutions, governments, and individuals.

Goldman Sachs seeks out people with all types of skills, interests and experiences. There's no template for the "right" Goldman Sachs employee, which is why they search for talent in new places and in new ways, seeking different majors, personalities, experiences, skills, and working styles.

For them, it's all about bringing together people who are curious, collaborative, and have the drive to make things possible for their clients and communities.

With 70+ offices and 36,000+ people, Goldman Sachs is constantly evolving and innovating to shape the future of finance and to help its clients in an ever-changing world.

The Goldman Sachs culture fosters an environment that enables colleagues to fulfil their highest aspirations, both professionally and personally. From digital learning and leadership development training to resilience and mindfulness offerings, they are invested in all aspects of their workforce and are committed to growth at every level.

At Goldman Sachs, their goal is to attract the extraordinarily talented and diverse people needed to drive their business into the future. Diversity and inclusion is a business imperative and they strive to cultivate a work experience where their people can reach their full potential and thrive as their authentic selves. For Goldman Sachs' people to excel, everyone must feel that they are operating in an inclusive environment that celebrates differences and values different ways of thinking.

GRADUATE VACANCIES IN 2022

ACCOUNTANCY
ENGINEERING
FINANCE
HUMAN RESOURCES
INVESTMENT BANKING
LAW
RESEARCH & DEVELOPMENT
SALES
TECHNOLOGY

NUMBER OF VACANCIES
400 graduate jobs

LOCATIONS OF VACANCIES

Vacancies also available worldwide.

STARTING SALARY FOR 2022
£Competitive
Plus a competitive bonus and a relocation allowance.

WORK EXPERIENCE

INSIGHT COURSES | DEGREE PLACEMENTS | SUMMER INTERNSHIPS

UNIVERSITY PROMOTIONS DURING 2021-2022
ASTON, BATH, BIRMINGHAM, BRISTOL, CAMBRIDGE, CARDIFF, CITY, DURHAM, EDINBURGH, EXETER, GLASGOW, IMPERIAL COLLEGE LONDON, KING'S COLLEGE LONDON, LANCASTER, LEEDS, LSE, LOUGHBOROUGH, MANCHESTER, NEWCASTLE, NOTTINGHAM, OXFORD, QMUL, SHEFFIELD, SOUTHAMPTON, ST ANDREWS, SURREY, UCL, WARWICK, YORK

APPLICATION DEADLINE
21st November 2021

FURTHER INFORMATION
www.Top100GraduateEmployers.com
Register now for the latest news, local promotions, work experience and graduate vacancies at Goldman Sachs.

Curious, collaborative and driven? Let's chat.

See yourself here.

At Goldman Sachs, we believe who you are makes you better at what you do. We seek out people with all types of skills, interests and experiences. Even if you have never imagined a career in finance, there's a place for you here. For us, it's all about bringing together people who are curious, collaborative and have the drive to make things possible for our clients and communities.

Interested? We'd love to meet you – join us at our upcoming events or programmes to meet us and learn more about the opportunities we offer.

EMEA APPLICATION DEADLINES

We review applications on a rolling basis and encourage you to apply as soon as you are ready.

21 November 2021

- New Analyst Programme (excl. Engineering/Warsaw)
- Summer Analyst Programme (excl. Engineering/Warsaw)
- Spring Programme
- Work Placement Programmee

30 January 2022

- Engineering New Analyst and Summer Analyst

Rolling Deadlines

- Warsaw (All Programmes)
- EMEA Off-Cycle Programmes
- Goldman Sachs Insight Events and Exploratory Programmes

Make things possible.

Google

Larry Page and Sergey Brin founded Google in September 1998 with a mission to organise the world's information and make it universally accessible and useful. Since then, the company has grown to more than 120,000 employees worldwide, with a wide range of popular products and platforms.

A problem isn't truly solved until it's solved for all.

Googlers build products that help create opportunities for everyone, whether down the street or across the globe. They bring insight, imagination, and a healthy disregard for the impossible. They bring everything that makes them unique. It's really the people that make Google the kind of company it is. Google hires people who are smart and determined, and favours their ability over their experience.

Google hires graduates from all disciplines, from humanities and business-related courses to engineering and computer science. The ideal candidate is someone who can demonstrate a passion for the online industry and someone who has made the most of their time at university through involvement in clubs, societies, or relevant internships. Google hires graduates who have a variety of strengths and passions, not just isolated skill sets. For technical roles within engineering teams, specific skills will be required. The diversity of perspectives, ideas, and cultures – both within Google and in the tech industry overall – leads to the creation of better products and services.

Whether it's providing online marketing consultancy, selling an advertising solution to clients, hiring the next generation of Googlers, or building products, Google has full-time roles and internships available across teams like global customer solutions, sales, people operations, legal, finance, operations, cloud, and engineering.

GRADUATE VACANCIES IN 2022
CONSULTING
ENGINEERING
HUMAN RESOURCES
MARKETING
SALES
TECHNOLOGY

NUMBER OF VACANCIES
No fixed quota

LOCATIONS OF VACANCIES

Vacancies also available in Europe.

STARTING SALARY FOR 2022
£Competitive

WORK EXPERIENCE
SUMMER INTERNSHIPS

UNIVERSITY PROMOTIONS DURING 2021-2022
Please check with your university careers service for full details of Google's local promotions and events.

MINIMUM ENTRY REQUIREMENTS
Relevant degree required for some roles.

APPLICATION DEADLINE
Year-round recruitment

FURTHER INFORMATION
www.Top100GraduateEmployers.com
Register now for the latest news, local promotions, work experience and graduate vacancies at Google.

**Build
for
everyone**

Together, we can
create opportunities
for people to learn, be
heard, and succeed.
google.com/students

Google

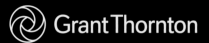

GRADUATE VACANCIES IN 2022

ACCOUNTANCY
CONSULTING
FINANCE

NUMBER OF VACANCIES
350-400 graduate jobs

LOCATIONS OF VACANCIES

STARTING SALARY FOR 2022
£Competitive

As one of the world's leading independent audit, tax, and advisory firms, Grant Thornton is a team of independent thinkers who put quality, inclusion, and integrity first. Offering a different experience to their clients all around the world. A better experience. Delivering expertise in a way that goes beyond.

Embracing uniqueness, the culture at Grant Thornton thrives on the contributions of all the people who work there – they never settle for what is easy, and they look beyond to deliver the right thing, for everyone.

On the Grant Thornton graduate programme, there's training and support to start thriving in no time. Within three years, graduates become professionally qualified, specialising in either audit, tax, or advisory.

Covering the full range of clients, experiences are truly there for the taking. And with exposure to clients from early on in their career, trainees will take on real responsibility and benefit from the knowledge and experience of colleagues.

Grant Thornton's flat structure gives trainees amazing opportunities to interact with senior business figures early in their career, and – with support from managers and exceptional training opportunities – the firm will do everything they can to help build the foundations for a great professional career.

Once qualified, the opportunities for graduates open up even further. They can keep progressing in their team, explore a different business area, or travel abroad and work at one of the 135 Grant Thornton member firms around the world.

The firm care more about an individual's potential than academic achievements alone. Helping to get graduates' working lives off to a flying start. Grant Thornton is looking for people who can add value, spark fresh ideas, and go beyond expectations. People that want to be able to proudly do what's right – for the firm, their colleagues, and their clients. It's how it should be.

WORK EXPERIENCE

DEGREE PLACEMENTS   SUMMER INTERNSHIPS

UNIVERSITY PROMOTIONS DURING 2021-2022
Please check with your university careers service for full details of Grant Thornton's local promotions and events.

MINIMUM ENTRY REQUIREMENTS
Any degree accepted

APPLICATION DEADLINE
Year-round recruitment
Early application is advised.

FURTHER INFORMATION
www.Top100GraduateEmployers.com
Register now for the latest news, local promotions, work experience and graduate vacancies at Grant Thornton.

GREAT MINDS. NOTHING ALIKE.

If they were, we wouldn't be where we are today.
Difference of opinion is something we celebrate,
and we'll back you so you can back yourself.
Freeing up your time and energy to unlock ideas
and innovations that propel our clients, and your
career, forward. We value your potential as much
as your academic achievements. **It's how it should be.**

Audit | Tax | Advisory

Visit **trainees.grantthornton.co.uk** to learn more

 Grant Thornton

HERBERT SMITH FREEHILLS

careers.herbertsmithfreehills.com/uk/grads

graduates.uk@hsf.com

linkedin.com/company/herbert-smith-freehills   facebook.com/HSFgraduatesUK

instagram.com/HSFgraduatesUK youtube.com/HSFgraduates

Herbert Smith Freehills is a leading, full-service international law firm that works on some of the most important cases and deals for the world's biggest organisations. As the world continues to evolve at an unprecedented pace, they are continuing to build a reputation for excellence.

Defined by their inclusive culture and commitment to innovation, Herbert Smith Freehills give trainees the platform and responsibility to make an impact from day one. They are inviting graduates to take control of their career and make progress to be proud of.

Few operate at the forefront of so many exciting sectors, combining legal expertise with a global perspective and local insight. With over 3,000 lawyers in 26 international offices, their leading international teams include an award-winning in-house advocacy unit and dispute resolution team, which is recognised as number one globally.

That exceptional performance is due to innovation and hard work being at the heart of everything they do. At Herbert Smith Freehills, it's less about watching from the sidelines and more about hitting the ground running, making a difference, and tackling big issues. That means everyone is expected to bring new ideas and skills to the work they do and to how they do it. All lawyers, including graduates, harness the latest technology to drive better outcomes and deliver innovations.

All trainees tailor their training contracts and sit in a range of practice groups, including the firm's leading corporate and disputes teams. They are given real responsibility across fee-earning work and pro bono initiatives. Here, trainees get the combination of a global and progressive approach that provides challenge that requires intellectual agility and a relentless drive to elevate their ambition.

GRADUATE VACANCIES IN 2022
LAW

NUMBER OF VACANCIES
60 graduate jobs
For training contracts starting in 2024.

LOCATIONS OF VACANCIES

STARTING SALARY FOR 2022
£47,000

UNIVERSITY PROMOTIONS DURING 2021-2022
BIRMINGHAM, BRISTOL, CAMBRIDGE, DURHAM, EDINBURGH, ESSEX, EXETER, GLASGOW, IMPERIAL COLLEGE LONDON, KING'S COLLEGE LONDON, KENT, LEEDS, LEICESTER, LIVERPOOL, LONDON SCHOOL OF ECONOMICS, MANCHESTER, NOTTINGHAM, OXFORD, QUEEN MARY LONDON, SHEFFIELD, SOUTHAMPTON, UEA, UNIVERSITY COLLEGE LONDON, WARWICK, YORK

MINIMUM ENTRY REQUIREMENTS
2.1 Degree

APPLICATION DEADLINE
3rd December 2021
For spring and summer vacation schemes. See website for other deadlines.

FURTHER INFORMATION
www.Top100GraduateEmployers.com
Register now for the latest news, local promotions, work experience and graduate vacancies at HSF.

HERBERT
SMITH
FREEHILLS

ELEVATE YOUR
AMBITION

26
OFFICES
GLOBALLY

14 🌐
INTERNATIONAL
SECONDMENTS

£47K
IN FIRST
YEAR

26,897
HOURS OF
PRO BONO
& CSR ADVICE

GLOBAL
INNOVATION
AWARD 2020
RELATIVITY FEST

INCLUSIVE   CHALLENGING   PROGRESSIVE   DIVERSE   INNOVATIVE

CAREERS.HERBERTSMITHFREEHILLS.COM/UK/GRADS

graduates.hoganlovells.com

graduate.recruitment@hoganlovells.com

twitter.com/HLgraduatesUK   facebook.com/HoganLovellsGradsUK

instagram.com/HoganLovellsGradsUK   linkedin.com/company/hoganlovells

Defined by Difference. It's a statement of who Hogan Lovells are. It's the guiding principle that governs how they think, act, and evolve. Across their 46 offices, their 2,600+ lawyers focus on exceeding expectations. They're out there championing innovation, crossing borders, and shaping legal precedents.

How? It takes agility and ambition to stay ahead. Which is why Hogan Lovells continue to offer opportunities to students looking to get to know the firm. From vacation schemes to insight events, law fairs, webinars, workshops, and more, all their opportunities are packed with insight and practical experience. Students will meet Hogan Lovells lawyers, delve into broad practice groups and high-profile projects, develop their own commercial awareness, and learn more about the role of a trainee solicitor.

The firm's two-year training contract focuses on practical hands-on learning guided by experienced colleagues. Graduates develop a deep understanding of Hogan Lovells' bold and distinctive approach to collaborating to create valuable global solutions, as they learn from a diverse network of industry leading lawyers.

Here's how it works: graduates do four six-month seats across different practice groups – Corporate and Finance, Global Regulatory and Intellectual Property, Media and Technology, Litigation Arbitration, and Employment. Plus, for one of those seats, they'll have the chance to apply for an international or client secondment.

No matter where they come from or which path they take, Hogan Lovells provide graduates with opportunities to grow their legal acumen, sharpen their commercial edge, and tackle real challenges presented by major global clients in new and exciting ways. By supporting and encouraging them at every point in their career, they're helping them to define their own difference too.

GRADUATE VACANCIES IN 2022

LAW

NUMBER OF VACANCIES
Up to 50 graduate jobs
For training contracts starting in 2024.

LOCATIONS OF VACANCIES

STARTING SALARY FOR 2022
£47,500

UNIVERSITY PROMOTIONS DURING 2021-2022
Please check with your university careers service for full details of Hogan Lovells' local promotions and events.

MINIMUM ENTRY REQUIREMENTS
2.1 Degree

APPLICATION DEADLINE
Law: 31st July 2022
Non-Law: 31st January 2022

FURTHER INFORMATION
www.Top100GraduateEmployers.com
Register now for the latest news, local promotions, work experience and graduate vacancies at Hogan Lovells.

HSBC

With a global network across 64 countries and territories, serving more than 40 million customers, HSBC is one of the world's largest and most connected banking and financial services organisations. It is focused on opening up a world of opportunity.

HSBC is looking for students and graduates who are collaborative in action and curious thinkers – individuals with the courage to challenge the status quo and the motivation to make a positive impact for the customers they serve and the communities in which they operate.

HSBC is focused on building a sustainable future and serving the needs of a changing world. The company knows that economic growth must be sustainable for colleagues, customers, and communities. HSBC is focused on the importance of providing sustainable financial solutions to support customers in their transition to net zero – all while speeding up its own transition to becoming a net zero bank.

HSBC puts diversity at the heart of its business and provides an open, supportive, and inclusive working environment, with tailored training and support to help employees thrive on their chosen career path. No matter what interests and skills they might have, a career at HSBC will offer the opportunities, experiences, networks, and training needed – so there's no limit to how far they can go as part of an international and connected workforce.

Students and graduates can apply to join HSBC's local or global intern and graduate programmes across the bank in the following areas: Commercial Banking, Global Banking & Markets, Wealth and Personal Banking (including Global Asset Management and Private Banking), or Digital Business Services, including Operations and Technology.

GRADUATE VACANCIES IN 2022

ACCOUNTANCY
FINANCE
GENERAL MANAGEMENT
INVESTMENT BANKING
RETAIL
TECHNOLOGY

NUMBER OF VACANCIES
600+ graduate jobs

LOCATIONS OF VACANCIES

Vacancies also available worldwide.

STARTING SALARY FOR 2022
£Competitive

WORK EXPERIENCE

DEGREE PLACEMENTS   SUMMER INTERNSHIPS

UNIVERSITY PROMOTIONS DURING 2021-2022

ABERDEEN, ABERYSTWYTH, ASTON, BANGOR, BATH, BELFAST, BIRMINGHAM, BRADFORD, BRISTOL, BRUNEL, CAMBRIDGE, CARDIFF, CITY, DUNDEE, DURHAM, EDINBURGH, ESSEX, EXETER, GLASGOW, HERIOT-WATT, HULL, IMPERIAL COLLEGE LONDON, KEELE, KING'S COLLEGE LONDON, KENT, LANCASTER, LEEDS, LEICESTER, LIVERPOOL, LSE, LOUGHBOROUGH, MANCHESTER, NEWCASTLE, NORTHUMBRIA, NOTTINGHAM, NOTTINGHAM TRENT, OXFORD, OXFORD BROOKES, PLYMOUTH, QMUL, READING, ROYAL HOLLOWAY, SOAS, SHEFFIELD, SOUTHAMPTON, ST ANDREWS, STIRLING, STRATHCLYDE, SURREY, SUSSEX, SWANSEA, UEA, ULSTER, UCL, WARWICK, YORK

MINIMUM ENTRY REQUIREMENTS
Varies by function
Relevant degree required for some roles.

APPLICATION DEADLINE
Varies by function

FURTHER INFORMATION
www.Top100GraduateEmployers.com
Register now for the latest news, local promotions, work experience and graduate vacancies at HSBC.

You want
to make
an impact

We'll give you
a world of
support to do it

You're interested in becoming a part of our global community. We'll connect you with our diverse network, all working towards a common goal. And we'll help you embrace the possibilities and shared experiences of learning.

Discover a world of opportunities with our global intern and graduate programmes at hsbc.com/earlycareers

 HSBC

Together we thrive

As the largest commercial television network in the UK, ITV have what it takes to make it together, make it new, and make it brilliant. It's the reason they already offer some of the biggest career opportunities in the industry. Together, they're turning their ambition to be More than TV into reality.

ITV's strategic vision is to be a digitally led media and entertainment company that creates and brings its brilliant content to audiences wherever, whenever, and however they choose; this is aligned to its purpose to be More than TV.

ITV connects millions of people every day, makes content they can't get enough of, and reflects and shapes the world they live in... and their teams do all this through the power of creativity. ITV is the largest free-to-air commercial television network in the UK and is a leading creative force in global content production and distribution, with over 55 labels. Creativity, quality content, and engaging audiences in the UK and around the world is at the core of everything they do.

Their teams are the masterminds who keep ITV's channels packed with the best in high quality programming. That means dramas, soaps, celebrity, reality, factual programming, news, sport, and more. They also ensure that they knit the commercial side together with the creative side of their business. The teams in ITV Commercial are responsible for strategically partnering with agencies and advertisers building new digital capabilities and delivering data-driven TV advertising by creatively integrating brands with their content. They also offer Corporate roles in Marketing, Creative, Technology & Operations, Finance, Legal, HR, Group Comms, Data & AI, Audience Research, and more.

Their Technology Graduate Programmes offer a two-year rotational programme working across areas such as Software Engineering, Data, Cyber Security, and Networking, or a two-year AI- and Data-focused programme.

GRADUATE VACANCIES IN 2022

ACCOUNTANCY
FINANCE
GENERAL MANAGEMENT
HUMAN RESOURCES
LAW
MARKETING
MEDIA
RESEARCH & DEVELOPMENT
SALES
TECHNOLOGY

NUMBER OF VACANCIES
No fixed quota

LOCATIONS OF VACANCIES

STARTING SALARY FOR 2022
£Competitive

WORK EXPERIENCE
INSIGHT COURSES | DEGREE PLACEMENTS | SUMMER INTERNSHIPS

UNIVERSITY PROMOTIONS DURING 2021-2022
Please check with your university careers service for full details of ITV's local promotions and events.

MINIMUM ENTRY REQUIREMENTS
2.2 Degree
Relevant degree required for some roles.

APPLICATION DEADLINE
Varies by function

FURTHER INFORMATION
www.Top100GraduateEmployers.com
Register now for the latest news, local promotions, work experience and graduate vacancies at ITV.

Build an incredible career – the ITV Way.

In their offices and studios, they love celebrating individuality and they're committed to creating an organisation where everyone feels included. This means building a diverse and creative team that represents everyone, that gives people the opportunity to thrive, and where everyone can feel valued.

Find out why we are More than TV at itvjobs.com

J.P.Morgan

J.P. Morgan are committed to helping businesses and markets grow and develop in more than 100 countries. Over the last 200 years, they have evolved to meet the complex financial needs of some of the world's largest companies, as well as many of the smaller businesses driving industry change.

J.P. Morgan work hard to do the right thing for their clients, shareholders, and the firm every day. Joining the firm means learning from experts in a collaborative team environment where successful applicants will be supported to make an immediate impact from the start.

Whilst academic achievements are important, they're also looking for individuality and passion, as demonstrated by extra-curricular activities. J.P. Morgan invest in helping graduates fulfil their potential as they build their career at the firm. Internship and graduate positions are available firmwide, so applicants are encouraged to learn as much as possible about the different business areas and roles. They also offer pre-internship programmes, such as Early Insights, which provide insight into the finance industry and their programmes. They often hire directly from these opportunities – giving successful applicants early exposure to the firm and how they do business. The internship and full-time programmes they hire into are: asset management, corporate analyst development, data science & machine learning, global finance & business management, human resources, investment banking, markets, quantitative research, risk, software engineer, tech connect, wealth management, wholesale payments, and corporate banking.

Working with a team committed to doing their best, earning the trust of their clients, and encouraging employees to fulfil their potential – that's what it means to be part of J.P. Morgan.

GRADUATE VACANCIES IN 2022
ACCOUNTANCY
FINANCE
GENERAL MANAGEMENT
HUMAN RESOURCES
INVESTMENT BANKING
TECHNOLOGY

NUMBER OF VACANCIES
500 graduate jobs

LOCATIONS OF VACANCIES

Vacancies also available in Europe.

STARTING SALARY FOR 2022
£Competitive
Plus a competitive bonus.

WORK EXPERIENCE
| INSIGHT COURSES | DEGREE PLACEMENTS | SUMMER INTERNSHIPS |

UNIVERSITY PROMOTIONS DURING 2021-2022
Please check with your university careers service for full details of J.P. Morgan's local promotions and events.

APPLICATION DEADLINE
28th November 2021

FURTHER INFORMATION
www.Top100GraduateEmployers.com
Register now for the latest news, local promotions, work experience and graduate vacancies at J.P. Morgan.

J.P.Morgan

Choose a career with choice

We're looking for students from all majors and backgrounds to join our diverse, global team.

As a top employer in financial services, J.P. Morgan does much more than manage money. Here, you'll have more chances to continuously innovate, learn and make a positive impact for our clients, customers and communities.

We offer internships in over 12 different business areas as well as Early Insight Programs to introduce you to the industry and our company.

jpmorgan.com/careers

Biko | Automated Trading   **Susan** | Strategy Associate   **Ami** | Equity Research Associate

kpmgcareers.co.uk

facebook.com/KPMGrecruitment **f**   graduate@kpmg.co.uk ✉
linkedin.com/company/kpmg-advisory **in**   twitter.com/KPMGrecruitment **y**
instagram.com/KPMGtraineesUK 📷   youtube.com/KPMGrecruitmentUK ▶

KPMG in the UK is part of a global network of member firms that offers Audit, Tax, Legal, Consulting, Deal Advisory, and Technology services. Powered by the talent of around 16,000 people, the firm brings creativity, insight, and experience to solve their clients' and communities' biggest problems.

The firm's largest practice is Audit, which audits a quarter of the FTSE 100 firms and has a relentless focus on audit quality. In Tax & Law, Consulting, Deal Advisory, and Technology & Engineering, KPMG helps companies solve some of their most complex business challenges and make a meaningful impact.

Like the organisations they work with, KPMG is truly embracing change. From new ways of working to inspiring workspaces and innovative technology, people are empowered and equipped to deliver ground-breaking work with real flexibility.

KPMG aims to be universally recognised as a place where great people can come and do their best work. It's known for its collaborative culture, with people who are incredibly motivated and inquisitive, diverse in background and perspective, who believe in better, and are committed to delivering extraordinary results.

In return for all their hard work, trainees benefit from funded, relevant professional qualifications or accreditations, structured development, and the opportunity to build a truly rewarding long-term career. They are also encouraged to make a difference through a broad range of KPMG employee networks, volunteering, and community initiatives.

Joining KPMG means working alongside some of the brightest minds in business, supporting the UK in a connected world, and being part of an inclusive environment where everyone is empowered to spark debate, innovate, and bring about change.

GRADUATE VACANCIES IN 2022

ACCOUNTANCY
CONSULTING
FINANCE
GENERAL MANAGEMENT
LAW
TECHNOLOGY

NUMBER OF VACANCIES
1,000+ graduate jobs

LOCATIONS OF VACANCIES

STARTING SALARY FOR 2022
£Competitive
Plus a great range of rewards and benefits – see website for details.

WORK EXPERIENCE

INSIGHT COURSES | DEGREE PLACEMENTS | SUMMER INTERNSHIPS

UNIVERSITY PROMOTIONS DURING 2021-2022
ABERDEEN, ASTON, BATH, BIRMINGHAM, BRISTOL, CAMBRIDGE, CARDIFF, CITY, DUNDEE, DURHAM, EDINBURGH, ESSEX, EXETER, GLASGOW, HERIOT-WATT, IMPERIAL COLLEGE LONDON, KING'S COLLEGE LONDON, LANCASTER, LEEDS, LEICESTER, LIVERPOOL, LSE, LOUGHBOROUGH, MANCHESTER, NEWCASTLE, NORTHUMBRIA, NOTTINGHAM, NOTTINGHAM TRENT, OXFORD, PLYMOUTH, QMUL, READING, ROYAL HOLLOWAY, SALFORD, SHEFFIELD, SOUTHAMPTON, ST ANDREWS, STRATHCLYDE, SURREY, UEA, UCL, WARWICK, YORK

MINIMUM ENTRY REQUIREMENTS
2.1 Degree, 120 UCAS points
Degree in any discipline.
300 UCAS points for those who passed exams before 2017.
Please see website for details.

APPLICATION DEADLINE
Year-round recruitment
Early application is advised.

FURTHER INFORMATION
www.Top100GraduateEmployers.com
Register now for the latest news, local promotions, work experience and graduate vacancies at KPMG.

What if you could run and not worry about pollution?

Audit, Tax & Law, Consulting, Deal Advisory, Technology & Engineering

By taking a simple idea and working together with businesses across the UK to turn it into a real life tech tool, we can contribute to making a positive impact on the environment, and the world.

Discover graduate opportunities
kpmgcareers.co.uk

To imagine, is to do.

kubrïck

Redefining business for tomorrow takes a fresh approach today. The greatest data and technology challenges can't be solved with carbon copy consultants. Kubrick exists in order to solve the growing skills emergency which is undermining the development of society and organisations across the globe.

Kubrick's mission is to shape tomorrow's world by developing today's talent. They achieve this by increasing the size and diversity of the workforce and equipping them with cutting-edge skills that enable businesses to transform. Kubrick actively seek out and develop passionate individuals from a breadth of backgrounds to help organisations harness the power of next-generation technology.

Named the fastest-growing consultancy in Europe and the 17th fastest-growing company overall in the coveted Financial Times 1000, Kubrick are experts in unleashing the potential in humans and technology. As an organisation, they recognise the power of diversity of thought and experience, and are champions of women in technology, with over three times the industry average of females in technology roles.

Kubrick offer unrivalled training designed and delivered by industry experts, which replicates the real working environment. This training is divided into five unique practices that prepare consultants for different areas and roles within data and next-generation technology: Data Engineering, Data Product, Data Management, Machine Learning Engineering, and Cloud Engineering. These roles are in great demand in today's business environment, building a foundation of skills to support rapid career development for the long-term. After completing the programme, consultants are matched to client engagements to help organisations across all industries revolutionise their capabilities.

GRADUATE VACANCIES IN 2022

CONSULTING

TECHNOLOGY

NUMBER OF VACANCIES
610 graduate jobs

LOCATIONS OF VACANCIES

STARTING SALARY FOR 2022
£32,000
Including salaried 15-week training.

UNIVERSITY PROMOTIONS DURING 2021-2022
Please check with your university careers service for full details of Kubrick's local promotions and events.

MINIMUM ENTRY REQUIREMENTS
2.1 Degree

APPLICATION DEADLINE
Year-round recruitment
Early application is advised.

FURTHER INFORMATION
www.Top100GraduateEmployers.com
Register now for the latest news, local promotions, work experience and graduate vacancies at Kubrick.

Shape your tomorrow, today

Our industry-leading, paid training gives our consultants the skills to change the future.

kubrick

Become a leader in next-generation technology.

kubrickgroup.com/join-us

Nikita Mandavia
Data Management Consultant

L'ORÉAL

L'Oréal is the world's number one beauty company, with a portfolio of 36 international brands including L'Oréal Paris, Garnier, and Lancôme, to name a few. L'Oréal's ambition is to become the world's leading beauty tech company, through digital innovation, product design, and world-class consumer journeys.

L'Oréal UK and Ireland, the local subsidiary and leading player in the multi-billion-pound beauty industry in the UK, look for an entrepreneurial mindset in their graduates. They also believe in developing their people from the ground up, providing their employees with the opportunity to grow within the company and build a career with them. As a result, a portion of management trainee roles are filled by individuals from their internship and spring insight programmes, creating a well-rounded junior talent journey at L'Oréal. The remainder of the graduate roles are sourced from the external market, to ensure an equal opportunity for all potential candidates to join this exciting business.

On the Management Trainee Programme, graduates work in functions across the business, gaining a sense of life at L'Oréal. With three different rotations in their chosen stream, graduates are free to develop their talent and discover new possibilities, shaping their future careers as they go. With on-the-job training and their own HR Sponsor, graduates will progress into operational roles in as little as 18 months.

L'Oréal UKI is committed to being one of the top employers in the UK, fostering a workplace where everyone feels welcome and valued. Promoting gender equality, driving diversity and inclusion, addressing mental health, and establishing evolving workplace practices are a key focus. Through 'L'Oréal for the Future', L'Oréal's global sustainability programme, the business is driving change across all areas including product design, packaging, supply chain, and consumer behaviour.

GRADUATE VACANCIES IN 2022
FINANCE
GENERAL MANAGEMENT
MARKETING
SALES

NUMBER OF VACANCIES
30 graduate jobs

LOCATIONS OF VACANCIES

STARTING SALARY FOR 2022
£30,000

WORK EXPERIENCE
INSIGHT COURSES | DEGREE PLACEMENTS | SUMMER INTERNSHIPS

UNIVERSITY PROMOTIONS DURING 2021-2022
ASTON, BATH, BIRMINGHAM, BRISTOL, CAMBRIDGE, CARDIFF, DURHAM, EXETER, GLASGOW, IMPERIAL COLLEGE LONDON, KENT, LEEDS, LIVERPOOL, LONDON SCHOOL OF ECONOMICS, LOUGHBOROUGH, MANCHESTER, NEWCASTLE, NOTTINGHAM, NOTTINGHAM TRENT, SOUTHAMPTON, SUSSEX, WARWICK, YORK
Please check with your university careers service for full details of L'Oréal's local promotions and events.

APPLICATION DEADLINE
January 2022
Early application is advised.

FURTHER INFORMATION
www.Top100GraduateEmployers.com
Register now for the latest news, local promotions, work experience and graduate vacancies at L'Oréal.

FREEDOM TO
GO BEYOND,
THAT'S THE BEAUTY
OF L'ORÉAL.

L'ORÉAL

Our brands, dynamic culture, and a
mindset of always being our own
challenger, mean that we offer autonomy
and opportunities you won't get
anywhere else.

**At L'Oréal UK and Ireland you are trusted
to succeed.**

Graduate and Internship
opportunities at:
CAREERS.LOREAL.COM

GRADUATE VACANCIES IN 2022
LAW

NUMBER OF VACANCIES
24 graduate jobs
For training contracts starting in 2024.

LOCATIONS OF VACANCIES

STARTING SALARY FOR 2022
£50,000

WORK EXPERIENCE
INSIGHT COURSES | SUMMER INTERNSHIPS

UNIVERSITY PROMOTIONS DURING 2021-2022
BIRMINGHAM, BRISTOL, CAMBRIDGE, CARDIFF, DURHAM, EDINBURGH, EXETER, GLASGOW, KING'S COLLEGE LONDON, LEEDS, LONDON SCHOOL OF ECONOMICS, MANCHESTER, NOTTINGHAM, OXFORD, QUEEN MARY LONDON, ST ANDREWS, UNIVERSITY COLLEGE LONDON, WARWICK, YORK
Please check with your university careers service for full details of Latham & Watkins' local promotions and events.

MINIMUM ENTRY REQUIREMENTS
2.1 Degree

APPLICATION DEADLINE
Varies by function

FURTHER INFORMATION
www.Top100GraduateEmployers.com
*Register now for the latest news, local promotions, work experience and graduate vacancies at **Latham & Watkins**.*

Latham & Watkins is one of the world's largest law firms, with more than 3,000 attorneys in offices across Europe, the US, the Middle East, and Asia. The firm is a global leader in corporate transactions, environmental law, finance matters, litigations and trials, and tax services.

Latham & Watkins' non-hierarchical, collegiate management style and ambitious and entrepreneurial culture make it a unique place to work. Over 70% of the firm's transactions involve five or more offices, and the collaborative atmosphere is strengthened by the firm's diversity. Latham's global diversity strategy and initiatives work to strengthen and promote the firm as a workplace where the best and brightest attorneys from all groups excel and find the opportunities and support to fulfil their potential to become firm and industry leaders.

The firm offers exceptional training and support to ensure seamless collaboration on projects that span time zones, teams, and offices in the world's major financial, business, and regulatory centres. Latham is known for advising some of the world's leading corporates, financial institutions, and private equity firms on market-shaping transactions, disputes, and regulatory matters.

Pro bono is a cornerstone of Latham's culture. Since 2020, Latham has provided almost 4 million pro bono hours in free legal services to underserved individuals and families and the non-profit sector, valued at more than US$2 billion.

Latham offers a training contract with real responsibility, combined with supervision from market-leading lawyers on complex, high-profile, and cross-border work. The firm looks for outstanding people who have the potential to become exceptional lawyers. Initiative, communication skills, complex thinking, willingness to assume responsibility, resilience, and judgement are some of the traits particularly valued at Latham.

WHEN, *There's*
YOU *no limit*
JOIN *to what*
LATHAM *you can*
& WATKINS *achieve*

It won't be long before you're working on your own transactions and cases, instead of reading up on existing ones.

At Latham & Watkins, you'll get the chance to make a big impact in small teams. And you'll be surrounded by experts who are invested in seeing you succeed.

Discover the opportunities

LATHAM&WATKINS

Lidl are proud pioneers in the world of retail. With over 800 stores, 13 warehouses, and over 25,000 employees in the UK alone, they're one of the fastest growing retailers in the country. But it doesn't stop there. Ambitious plans for UK growth over the coming years show they don't like to stand still.

Challenging and changing the world of grocery retail, Lidl are more than just an average discount retailer. They are striving to make the experience exceptional for all, from customers to colleagues. Lidl is committed to driving various responsibility programmes, including charity partnerships, food redistribution, recycling schemes, and sustainability sourcing for the future.

Lidl is a fast-paced, dynamic business, and that's exactly what they are looking for in their graduates. They aren't just looking for one type of person. They are looking for ambitious, dedicated talent with personality and potential. Potential to become one of Lidl's future leaders.

Lidl's structured graduate programmes across all areas of the business are designed to develop graduates quickly. They have exciting opportunities for ambitious people who want to join their busy environment, where they'll be challenged to make progress and provide what people need.

Throughout the programme, graduates will gain soft skills alongside operational development through a bespoke and structured training plan, providing a clear development path. Graduates will learn from the best managers and develop their operational and management abilities from day one – progression from there is down to the individual.

Graduates benefit from competitive salaries, fast-tracked development, and stimulating work with world-class teams, all while working towards one goal: to feed the nation.

GRADUATE VACANCIES IN 2022

FINANCE
GENERAL MANAGEMENT
LOGISTICS
PROPERTY
PURCHASING
RETAIL
SALES

NUMBER OF VACANCIES
60+ graduate jobs

LOCATIONS OF VACANCIES

STARTING SALARY FOR 2022
£37,000

WORK EXPERIENCE
DEGREE
PLACEMENTS

UNIVERSITY PROMOTIONS DURING 2021-2022
ABERDEEN, ABERYSTWYTH, ASTON, BATH, BIRMINGHAM, BRISTOL, CARDIFF, EXETER, GLASGOW, HERIOT-WATT, KING'S COLLEGE LONDON, KENT, LEEDS, LIVERPOOL, LOUGHBOROUGH, MANCHESTER, NEWCASTLE, NOTTINGHAM, OXFORD, PLYMOUTH, READING, ST ANDREWS, SUSSEX, UNIVERSITY COLLEGE LONDON, YORK
Please check with your university careers service for full details of Lidl's local promotions and events.

MINIMUM ENTRY REQUIREMENTS
2.2 Degree

APPLICATION DEADLINE
December 2021

FURTHER INFORMATION
www.Top100GraduateEmployers.com
*Register now for the latest news, local promotions, work experience and graduate vacancies at **Lidl**.*

Raise your ambition

Opportunities as extraordinary as you

Week after week you'll build skills and confidence on our graduate programmes and find out what it takes to be part of an operation that feeds the nation.

Careers as extraordinary as you

Scan the QR code to find out more or visit our website:

 lidlgraduatecareers.co.uk

Linklaters

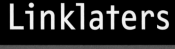

careers.linklaters.com

facebook.com/LinklatersGradsUK   trainee.recruitment@linklaters.com

linkedin.com/company/linklaters   twitter.com/LinklatersGrads

instagram.com/LinklatersGraduatesUK youtube.com/LinklatersCareers

From a shifting geopolitical landscape to the exponential growth in FinTech, this is a time of unprecedented change. Linklaters is ready. They go further to support clients, with market-leading legal insight and innovation. And they go further for each other, too.

When people join Linklaters, they find colleagues they want to work with. Inspiring, personable professionals who are generous with their time and always happy to help. Because, to be best in class, Linklaters looks for open-minded, team-spirited individuals who will collaborate – and innovate – to deliver the smartest solutions for clients.

Linklaters recruits candidates from a range of different backgrounds and disciplines, not just law. Why? Because those candidates bring with them a set of unique skills and perspectives that can help to challenge conventional thinking and inspire different approaches to client problems.

All Linklaters trainees benefit from pioneering learning and development opportunities and an inclusive working culture that encourages them to fulfil their potential.

Over two years, trainees take four six-month seats (placements) in different practice areas and sometimes abroad. They work on high-profile deals across a global network of 31 offices, and gain the knowledge they need to qualify. And, throughout their career, they enjoy the advantage of world-class training, courtesy of the Linklaters Learning & Development team.

With their uniquely future-focused culture and high-profile, global opportunities, Linklaters provides the ideal preparation for a rewarding career, no matter what the future holds.

Great change is here. Get ready.

GRADUATE VACANCIES IN 2022

LAW

NUMBER OF VACANCIES
100 graduate jobs
For training contracts starting in 2024.

LOCATIONS OF VACANCIES

STARTING SALARY FOR 2022
£50,000

WORK EXPERIENCE

INSIGHT COURSES   SUMMER INTERNSHIPS

UNIVERSITY PROMOTIONS DURING 2021-2022
BELFAST, BIRMINGHAM, BRISTOL, CAMBRIDGE, CARDIFF, CITY, DURHAM, EDINBURGH, EXETER, GLASGOW, KING'S COLLEGE LONDON, KENT, LANCASTER, LEEDS, LEICESTER, LONDON SCHOOL OF ECONOMICS, MANCHESTER, NEWCASTLE, NOTTINGHAM, NOTTINGHAM TRENT, OXFORD, OXFORD BROOKES, QUEEN MARY LONDON, SCHOOL OF AFRICAN STUDIES, SHEFFIELD, ST ANDREWS, SURREY, SUSSEX, SWANSEA, UEA, UNIVERSITY COLLEGE LONDON, WARWICK, YORK
Please check with your university careers service for full details of Linklaters' local promotions and events.

MINIMUM ENTRY REQUIREMENTS
2.1 Degree

APPLICATION DEADLINE
10th December 2021

FURTHER INFORMATION
www.Top100GraduateEmployers.com
*Register now for the latest news, local promotions, work experience and graduate vacancies at **Linklaters**.*

Great change is here.

Linklaters

Are you ready?

From a shifting geopolitical landscape
to the exponential growth in FinTech,
this is a time of unprecedented change.

At Linklaters, we're ready. Our people
go further to support our clients,
with market-leading legal insight and
innovation. And we go further for each
other, too. We're people you want to work
with, generous with our time and ready
to help. So no matter what the future
holds, with us you'll be one step ahead.
Great change is here. Get ready.

Find out more at careers.linklaters.com

As the UK's largest financial services group, with over 25 million customers, Lloyds Banking Group offers graduates a wide range of opportunities to make a real impact for customers, communities, and colleagues through brands like Lloyds Bank, Halifax, Bank of Scotland, and Scottish Widows.

The world is constantly evolving. New technology and new opportunities are affecting how people bank every day. To become the bank of the future and meet the ever-changing needs of their customers, Lloyds Banking Group is inviting graduates with a wide range of skills and experience to embark on a career with them.

Lloyds Banking Group is looking for graduates who are excited by rewarding challenges, who thrive in an inclusive culture, and who are inspired by the Group's purpose of Helping Britain Recover. Whether it's forming relationships with clients or developing the next generation of technology, graduates will be given opportunities to make a real difference.

At Lloyds Banking Group there are a variety of opportunities. Whether they choose Commercial Banking, Retail Banking, Software Engineering, Data Science, Finance, or Risk Management, graduates will be supported, through buddies and their teams, in achieving a relevant professional qualification or training to help them further their career with the Group.

Best of all, Lloyds Banking Group offers a friendly and supportive work environment, where learning is central, flexible working patterns and ongoing support are championed, and everyone is free to be themselves. This is because Lloyds Banking Group knows that people do their best work when they feel respected and happy.

Discover careers with real impact at Lloyds Banking Group.

GRADUATE VACANCIES IN 2022

ACCOUNTANCY
ENGINEERING
FINANCE
MARKETING
TECHNOLOGY

NUMBER OF VACANCIES
100+ graduate jobs

LOCATIONS OF VACANCIES

STARTING SALARY FOR 2022
£31,000-£45,000
Plus a discretionary bonus, a settling-in allowance, and flexible working.

WORK EXPERIENCE
DEGREE
PLACEMENTS

UNIVERSITY PROMOTIONS DURING 2021-2022
ASTON, BATH, BIRMINGHAM, BRISTOL, CAMBRIDGE, CARDIFF, DUNDEE, DURHAM, EDINBURGH, GLASGOW, IMPERIAL COLLEGE LONDON, KING'S COLLEGE LONDON, LEEDS, LEICESTER, LIVERPOOL, LONDON SCHOOL OF ECONOMICS, MANCHESTER, NEWCASTLE, NOTTINGHAM, OXFORD, QUEEN MARY LONDON, SHEFFIELD, ST ANDREWS, STRATHCLYDE, UEA, UNIVERSITY COLLEGE LONDON, WARWICK, YORK
Please check with your university careers service for full details of Lloyds Banking Group's local promotions and events.

MINIMUM ENTRY REQUIREMENTS
2.2 Degree

APPLICATION DEADLINE
Varies by function

FURTHER INFORMATION
www.Top100GraduateEmployers.com
*Register now for the latest news, local promotions, work experience and graduate vacancies at **LBG**.*

JOIN LORENA IN HELPING US BUILD THE BANK OF THE FUTURE

At Lloyds Banking Group, we're committed to meeting the changing needs of families, businesses and communities across the UK. Our purpose is to Help Britain Recover, and to make that happen, we rely on the knowledge and expertise of a talented group of people.

People like Lorena, who joined us as a Software Engineering Graduate. What Lorena loves most about her role is the level of support and encouragement she receives from her team on a daily basis.

If you're as driven as Lorena is, if you're as passionate about making a real, tangible difference, then we can offer you the chance to make that happen. Not only will you feel challenged and inspired, you'll also be welcomed into an inclusive community that cares about your personal growth and wellbeing too.

Discover careers with real impact at **lloydsbankinggrouptalent.com**.

MARS

For generations, families across the world – including the four-legged members – have loved Mars brands, products, and services. Mars is 130,000 Associates across 80 countries, working hard to create the world's most loved products, including M&M'S®, EXTRA®, PEDIGREE®, WHISKAS®, and Dolmio®.

Mars might be a global business, but it's more like a community than a corporate – it's still a private, family-owned business built up of a family of Associates. Associates at Mars are united and guided by The Five Principles – Quality, Responsibility, Mutuality, Efficiency, and Freedom; these are key to the culture and help Associates make decisions they are proud of.

The culture at Mars is relationship-driven – and it's how these relationships are built that's most important. Collaborating with others is key. Mars encourages open communication, as this builds relationships formed of trust and respect.

Mars wants to stretch and challenge Associates every day to help them reach their full potential. So, they take learning and development seriously – it makes good business sense for Mars to have people performing at the top of their game. With great line managers, mentors, coaches and peers, graduates will be supported the whole way. And they will support other Associates to learn and grow on their journey too.

At Mars, graduates are offered an unrivalled opportunity from day one. Mars wants everything they do to matter – from the smallest things to the largest – and Mars wants their work to make a positive impact on the world around them. Graduates will have endless support to develop both personally and professionally, creating a start today, to an exciting and rewarding career tomorrow.

Start your tomorrow, today, with Mars.

GRADUATE VACANCIES IN 2022
ENGINEERING
FINANCE
GENERAL MANAGEMENT
MARKETING
SALES
TECHNOLOGY

NUMBER OF VACANCIES
25 graduate jobs

LOCATIONS OF VACANCIES

STARTING SALARY FOR 2022
£32,000
Plus a £2,000 bonus.

UNIVERSITY PROMOTIONS DURING 2021-2022
ASTON, BATH, BIRMINGHAM, BRISTOL, CAMBRIDGE, DURHAM, EXETER, LEEDS, NOTTINGHAM, OXFORD, UNIVERSITY COLLEGE LONDON
Please check with your university careers service for full details of Mars' local promotions and events.

MINIMUM ENTRY REQUIREMENTS
2.1 Degree

APPLICATION DEADLINE
Varies by function

FURTHER INFORMATION
www.Top100GraduateEmployers.com
Register now for the latest news, local promotions, work experience and graduate vacancies at Mars.

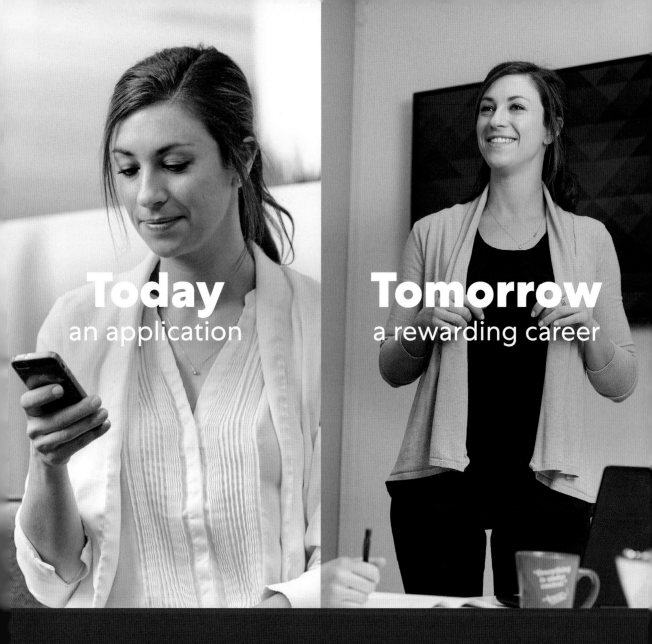

Today
an application

Tomorrow
a rewarding career

At Mars, the choices you make today shape the opportunities you get tomorrow. So whether you want to live and work in another country, have the freedom to move your career in any direction, or work on projects that make a difference to our world – you have the power to make it happen. Join one of our Graduate Leadership Experiences and get the support you need to start a brilliant career.

Visit **careers.mars.com/Students-Graduates**

#TomorrowStartsToday

MARS Your tomorrow starts today

mazars

jobs.mazars.co.uk/jobs

facebook.com/MazarsGroup   careers@mazars.co.uk
linkedin.com/company/mazars-in-uk twitter.com/Mazars_UK
instagram.com/MazarsLifeUK youtube.com/UKMazars

Mazars is an internationally integrated partnership, specialising in audit and accounting, tax, financial advisory, and consulting. Operating in over 90 countries and territories around the world, they draw on the expertise of more than 42,000 professionals.

Mazars is a positively different firm. Differentiated by the opportunities they offer their people, the way they work with clients, and their passion for responsible business. In the UK, Mazars is among the largest firms in its sector, employing over 2,300 people in 15 locations, providing a balanced perspective and empowered expertise, helping clients of all sizes make the most of business opportunities and operate with confidence.

The firm has a distinctive one-team approach where people are encouraged to grow and develop and to be their true self, whatever their background, culture, or generation. People are given responsibility and client exposure from the beginning of their career. The business has a coaching culture delivered through technical and soft skills training, mentorship, and one-to-one support.

Mazars' ethos ensures their people are trained to have the highest standards of technical excellence. Mazars offers the opportunity to gain a professional qualification whilst earning a competitive salary and gaining invaluable experience. These include the ACA, CA, ACCA, ATT/CTA, CII, CFAB, and an MSc in Applied Data Science, depending on the role.

Mazars is a leading international firm, aspiring to build the economic foundations of a fair and prosperous world. With sustainability, quality and integrity at their heart, Mazars encourages their people to develop a true sense of purpose which will make an impact and go beyond the day-to-day. Make a tangible difference and join Mazars today.

GRADUATE VACANCIES IN 2022
ACCOUNTANCY
CONSULTING
FINANCE
MARKETING
TECHNOLOGY

NUMBER OF VACANCIES
250+ graduate jobs

LOCATIONS OF VACANCIES

STARTING SALARY FOR 2022
£Competitive

WORK EXPERIENCE
DEGREE PLACEMENTS   SUMMER INTERNSHIPS

UNIVERSITY PROMOTIONS DURING 2021-2022
ABERYSTWYTH, ASTON, BATH, BIRMINGHAM, BRADFORD, BRISTOL, BRUNEL, CAMBRIDGE, CARDIFF, CITY, DURHAM, EDINBURGH, EXETER, GLASGOW, HERIOT-WATT, HULL, IMPERIAL COLLEGE LONDON, KING'S COLLEGE LONDON, KENT, LANCASTER, LEEDS, LEICESTER, LIVERPOOL, LSE, LOUGHBOROUGH, MANCHESTER, NEWCASTLE, NORTHUMBRIA, NOTTINGHAM, NOTTINGHAM TRENT, OXFORD, OXFORD BROOKES, PLYMOUTH, QMUL, READING, ROYAL HOLLOWAY, SHEFFIELD, SOUTHAMPTON, ST ANDREWS, STIRLING, STRATHCLYDE, SURREY, SUSSEX, UEA, UCL, WARWICK, YORK

MINIMUM ENTRY REQUIREMENTS
2.1 Degree, 112 UCAS points
Relevant degree required for some roles.

APPLICATION DEADLINE
Year-round recruitment
Early application is advised.

FURTHER INFORMATION
www.Top100GraduateEmployers.com
*Register now for the latest news, local promotions, work experience and graduate vacancies at **Mazars**.*

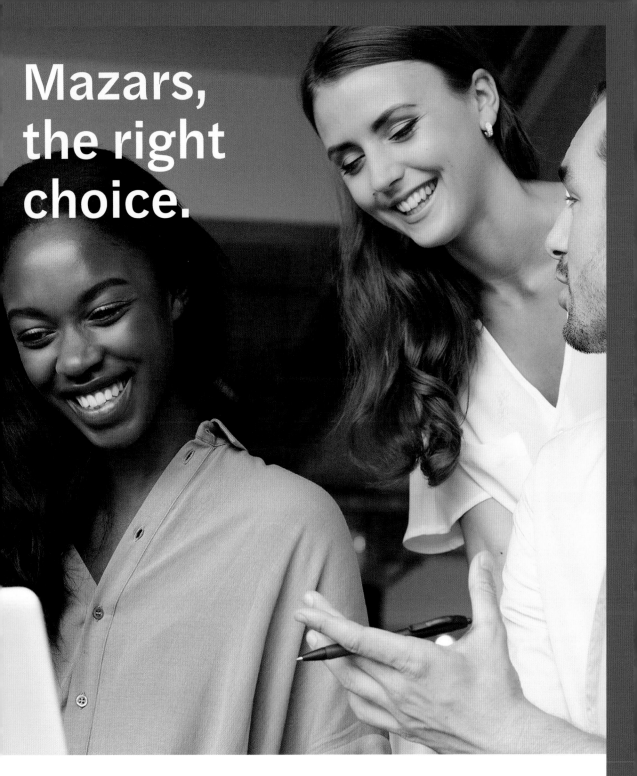

Mazars, the right choice.

As a leading international audit, tax and advisory firm, we aspire to help build the economic foundations of a fair and prosperous world by caring for the success of our people and clients, the health of the financial markets, and the integrity of our industry.

Commit to a future with purpose and come write the rest of (y)our story with us.

Find out more at jobs.mazars.co.uk

mazars

SECURITYSERVICE
MI5

MI5 helps safeguard the UK against threats to national security including terrorism and espionage. It investigates suspect individuals and organisations to gather intelligence relating to security threats. MI5 also advises the critical national infrastructure on protective security measures.

MI5 is a friendly, inclusive organisation which values diversity of background and diversity of thought. Graduates who join MI5 can expect stimulating and rewarding careers in a supportive environment, whilst enjoying a good work-life balance.

Many graduates join the Intelligence Officer Development Programme, which is a structured four-year programme designed to teach new joiners about MI5 investigations and to give them the skills to run them.

MI5 also deals with vast amounts of data, and interpreting that data is vital to its intelligence work. The Intelligence and Data Analyst Development Programme is a structured five-year programme which prepares individuals with potential to be part of this specialist career stream.

MI5 also offers a structured Technology Graduate Development Programme, which gives graduates the experience, knowledge, and skills they need to be an effective technology professional in the organisation's pioneering IT function.

Graduates who are looking for a rewarding career in corporate services can join MI5 as Business Enablers, where they can develop a breadth of experience undertaking corporate roles across a range of business areas, before having the opportunity to specialise in a particular area.

Graduates can also join as Russian or Mandarin analysts, working at the core of MI5's operational teams and using their language skills to provide intelligence insights.

GRADUATE VACANCIES IN 2022

FINANCE
GENERAL MANAGEMENT
HUMAN RESOURCES
INTELLIGENCE GATHERING
TECHNOLOGY

NUMBER OF VACANCIES
200+ graduate jobs

LOCATIONS OF VACANCIES

STARTING SALARY FOR 2022
£32,655+

WORK EXPERIENCE

INSIGHT COURSES | DEGREE PLACEMENTS | SUMMER INTERNSHIPS

UNIVERSITY PROMOTIONS DURING 2021-2022
Please check with your university careers service for full details of MI5's local promotions and events.

MINIMUM ENTRY REQUIREMENTS
2.2 Degree
Or relevant work experience.

APPLICATION DEADLINE
Varies by function

FURTHER INFORMATION
www.Top100GraduateEmployers.com
Register now for the latest news, local promotions, work experience and graduate vacancies at MI5.

Combine exciting opportunities

with fascinating work

to keep the country safe

Technology is rapidly evolving and it's vital for MI5 to stay one step ahead.
That is why we need graduates with a passion for technology who can come
up with innovative solutions to a wide range of technological challenges.
MI5 offers varied and rewarding careers in a supportive and encouraging
environment that puts the emphasis on teamwork. Whichever path you
choose you will be working with technology to help keep the country safe.

Discover your role at www.mi5.gov.uk/careers

Over the last four decades, Microsoft has helped people and organisations use technology to transform how they work, live, and play. Microsoft enables digital transformation for the era of an intelligent cloud and an intelligent edge, empowering every person and every organisation to achieve more.

Alongside traditional software engineering opportunities, Microsoft has graduate roles in project management, sales, and consulting. All graduates will be enrolled on their customised on-boarding process: Microsoft Aspire Experience. This two-year development programme is designed to equip top-performing graduates with the knowledge, tools, habits, and connections to thrive at Microsoft and to work across a broad range of roles.

The programme was built for those who thrive in dynamic environments and enjoy a challenge; who are quick to learn and adapt; who want to make an impact; and who believe that technology has the power to transform the world for the better.

Whatever a new joiner's skill set, Microsoft have positions available that will challenge and develop employees' current capabilities. Successful candidates gain valuable experience by working on real projects that have real impact. All Aspire graduates will be exposed to some of the brightest minds in the industry. Over the course of the programme, they will work alongside other Aspire graduates and build a network of connections in over 60 countries.

Microsoft don't just value difference, they seek it out and invite it in. They bring together people from across the globe and different walks of life – then support them with employee networks and employee resource groups.

Play a vital part in the business success of a high-tech global leader. Experience an inspiring world class programme. Start a Microsoft journey now.

GRADUATE VACANCIES IN 2022

CONSULTING
MARKETING
SALES
TECHNOLOGY

NUMBER OF VACANCIES
45 graduate jobs

LOCATIONS OF VACANCIES

Vacancies also available worldwide.

STARTING SALARY FOR 2022
£Competitive
Plus benefits.

WORK EXPERIENCE
DEGREE
PLACEMENTS

UNIVERSITY PROMOTIONS DURING 2021-2022
Please check with your university careers service for full details of Microsoft's local promotions and events.

MINIMUM ENTRY REQUIREMENTS
Varies by function
Relevant degree required for some roles.

APPLICATION DEADLINE
February 2022

FURTHER INFORMATION
www.Top100GraduateEmployers.com
Register now for the latest news, local promotions, work experience and graduate vacancies at Microsoft.

MAKE IT. BREAK IT. MAKE IT BETTER.

When smart, creative, passionate people get together, the result can be astounding and the opportunities limitless. Microsoft are looking ahead and empowering their customers to do more and achieve more. They are obsessing about building products to solve hard challenges. They are reinventing productivity. As a graduate you will help build the future in a cloud-first, mobile-first world.

www.microsoft.co.uk/students

 Microsoft

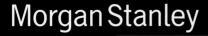

Morgan Stanley

morganstanley.com/campus

facebook.com/MorganStanley
linkedin.com/company/morgan-stanley twitter.com/MorganStanley
instagram.com/Morgan.Stanley youtube.com/MorganStanley

WE ARE
Morgan Stanley

Morgan Stanley is one of the world's leading financial services firms. They generate, manage, and distribute capital, helping businesses get the funds they need to develop innovative products and services that benefit millions. Their work is defined by the passion and dedication of their people.

Morgan Stanley's goals are achieved through hiring, training, and rewarding the best possible talent.

At Morgan Stanley, attitude is just as important as aptitude, and they want to work with and develop students and graduates who show integrity and commitment to their core values, who share their commitment to providing first-class client service, and who embrace change and innovation. Because the firm values a diversity of perspectives, it encourages people to be themselves and pursue their own interests.

There are numerous opportunities to learn, grow professionally, and help put the power of capital to work. All of Morgan Stanley's programmes are designed to provide the knowledge and toolkit graduates need to develop quickly into an effective and successful professional in their chosen area. Training is not limited to the first weeks or months on the job, but continues throughout a graduate's career. Over time, they could become part of the next generation of leaders, and play a part in technological, scientific, and cultural advancements that change the world forever.

Morgan Stanley believes that capital can work to benefit all. This success needs financial capital, but its foundation is intellectual capital. The talents and points of view of the diverse individuals working for them help to build their legacy and shape their future. This is why Morgan Stanley accepts applicants from all degree disciplines who demonstrate academic excellence.

GRADUATE VACANCIES IN 2022
FINANCE
HUMAN RESOURCES
INVESTMENT BANKING
SALES
TECHNOLOGY

NUMBER OF VACANCIES
200+ graduate jobs

LOCATIONS OF VACANCIES

STARTING SALARY FOR 2022
£Competitive

UNIVERSITY PROMOTIONS DURING 2021-2022
Please check with your university careers service for full details of Morgan Stanley's local promotions and events.

MINIMUM ENTRY REQUIREMENTS
2.1 Degree

APPLICATION DEADLINE
Varies by function

FURTHER INFORMATION
www.Top100GraduateEmployers.com
*Register now for the latest news, local promotions, work experience and graduate vacancies at **Morgan Stanley**.*

WE ARE IN SEARCH OF GREAT MINDS THAT THINK NOTHING ALIKE.

We believe our greatest asset is our people. We value our commitment to diverse perspectives and a culture of inclusion across the firm.

A career at Morgan Stanley means belonging to an ideas-driven culture that embraces new perspectives to solve complex problems.

Discover who we are.
morganstanley.com/campus

WE ARE
Morgan Stanley

Mariam
Bank Resource Management

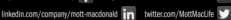

mottmac.com/careers/uk-and-ireland-graduate

facebook.com/MottMacDonaldGroup **f**   earlycareers.recruitment@mottmac.com ✉

linkedin.com/company/mott-macdonald **in**   twitter.com/MottMacLife 🐦

instagram.com/MottMacGroup 📷   youtube.com/MottMacDonald ▶

MOTT MACDONALD

Mott MacDonald is a global engineering, management, and development consultancy focused on guiding clients through many of the planet's most intricate challenges. By challenging norms and unlocking creativity, Mott MacDonald delivers long-lasting value for societies around the globe.

Mott MacDonald's purpose is to improve society by considering social outcomes in all they do, relentlessly focusing on excellence and digital innovation, transforming clients' businesses, their communities, and employee opportunities. Their 16,000-strong network of experts are joined up across sectors and geographies, giving their graduates access to an exceptional breadth of expertise and experience, enhancing their knowledge with the right support and guidance every step of the way. The consultancy's employees – active in 150 countries – take leading roles on some of the world's highest profile projects, turning obstacles into elegant, sustainable solutions. Individuals who get satisfaction from working on projects that benefit communities around the world will thrive at Mott MacDonald.

Additionally, as Mott MacDonald is an employee-owned company, it allows them to choose the work they take on and focus on the issues that are important.

Mott MacDonald's graduate schemes are more than just graduate jobs. With the help of a dedicated learning and development team, the accredited schemes aim to give graduates the opportunity to continually progress and develop in their chosen field.

All entry-level professionals are enrolled in Accelerating Your Future, a structured development programme that introduces key business and commercial competencies, enabling graduates to be the best that they can be.

GRADUATE VACANCIES IN 2022
CONSULTING
ENGINEERING
PROPERTY
TECHNOLOGY

NUMBER OF VACANCIES
300 graduate jobs

LOCATIONS OF VACANCIES

STARTING SALARY FOR 2022
£27,000-£31,000

WORK EXPERIENCE
DEGREE PLACEMENTS   SUMMER INTERNSHIPS

UNIVERSITY PROMOTIONS DURING 2021-2022
Please check with your university careers service for full details of Mott MacDonald's local promotions and events.

MINIMUM ENTRY REQUIREMENTS
Varies by function
Relevant degree required for some roles.

APPLICATION DEADLINE
14th November 2021

FURTHER INFORMATION
www.Top100GraduateEmployers.com
*Register now for the latest news, local promotions, work experience and graduate vacancies at **Mott MacDonald**.*

NatWest Group

jobs.natwestgroup.com

facebook.com/NatWestGroupEarlyCareers

linkedin.com/company/natwest-group | twitter.com/NWG_EarlyCareer

instagram.com/NatWestGroupEarlyCareers | NatWest Group Jobs

NatWest Group believes they succeed when their customers and their communities succeed as well. This is their purpose: to champion potential; helping people, families, and businesses to thrive. Their people are the foundation that success is built on, so they help them to thrive too.

Graduate, Intern, and Insight programmes at NatWest Group offer individuals structured and supported learning; making sure their potential comes first. With pathways allowing candidates to join the part of their business that suits them best, individuals can build a career they'll love. Their people are the foundation that success is built on, so they help colleagues to thrive by promising a fulfilling role, fair pay, excellent training, and great leadership.

Focusing on things they believe everyone shares – the need for financial security, the desire to improve a person's place in society, and the environment everyone lives in – NatWest Group aims to empower individuals and communities wherever they are. They use their expertise to share knowledge and skills which help people improve their financial wellbeing, through initiatives such as their longstanding MoneySense programme. They open doors to business and encourage entrepreneurship, particularly among underrepresented groups. And they're a major funder of renewable energy projects, while driving their own operations to carbon positive.

A career here means colleagues will benefit from an inclusive culture where individual strengths and working styles are appreciated and encouraged. And because of their significant investment in technology, no matter where people or their colleagues are based, working at NatWest Group is more flexible than it's ever been. Graduates and Interns collaborate across the organisation; getting the support they need to make a positive impact with the work they do.

GRADUATE VACANCIES IN 2022
FINANCE
HUMAN RESOURCES
TECHNOLOGY

NUMBER OF VACANCIES
260+ graduate jobs

LOCATIONS OF VACANCIES

STARTING SALARY FOR 2022
£31,850

WORK EXPERIENCE
SUMMER INTERNSHIPS

UNIVERSITY PROMOTIONS DURING 2021-2022
ABERDEEN, ASTON, BIRMINGHAM, BRISTOL, EDINBURGH, GLASGOW, LANCASTER, LEEDS, MANCHESTER, NOTTINGHAM, QUEEN MARY LONDON, STRATHCLYDE, WARWICK
Please check with your university careers service for full details of NatWest Group's local promotions and events.

MINIMUM ENTRY REQUIREMENTS
2.1 Degree

APPLICATION DEADLINE
Varies by function

FURTHER INFORMATION
www.Top100GraduateEmployers.com
Register now for the latest news, local promotions, work experience and graduate vacancies at **NatWest Group**.

We champion potential.

NatWest Group

Our purpose is to help people, families and businesses to thrive.

We want to build deep, lasting relationships with our customers – that's the best way for us to help them succeed. When our customers succeed, we succeed and become what people want us to be – resilient, sustainable and built for the long-term.

We know we're on a journey, but we're determined to see it through.

To help us achieve our purpose, we promise you a clear and fulfilling job – where you can be yourself, achieve a healthy work-life balance and see your career flourish.

Visit jobs.natwestgroup.com to explore our graduate and intern programmes.

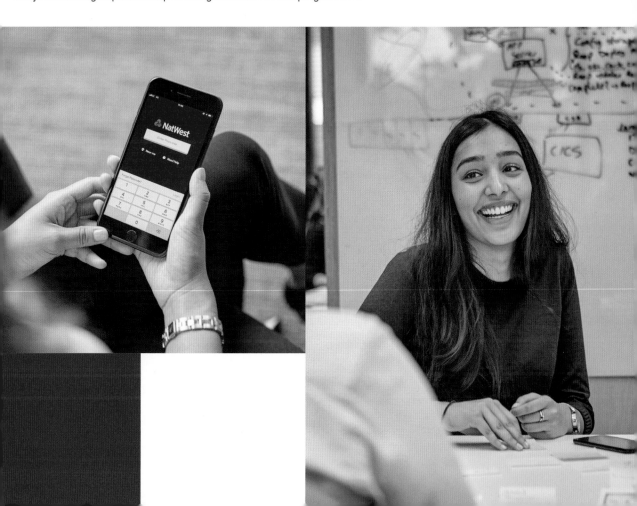

NEWTON

graduates@newtoneurope.com ✉

linkedin.com/company/newton-europe-limited **in**   facebook.com/NewtonEurope **f**

instagram.com/NewtonEurope ⓞ   youtube.com/NewtonEuropeLtd ▶

Newton is a consulting firm. But not like any other. Its people share a fundamental belief that every organisation can be better. And, along with everyone else at Newton, graduates play a big part in realising that potential. They make Newton stand out from others in the consulting space.

As specialists in operational improvement, Newton cracks some of the toughest business and public sector challenges around. Not with reports or copy-and-paste thinking. But by pinpointing and helping to deliver the changes that will make the biggest difference to their clients. And if they don't achieve the results they agree to at the start, they don't receive a fee.

For one client in the aerospace industry, that meant reducing its cost base by £8.3m. For another, in manufacturing, that meant slashing food waste by 16% and CO_2 emissions by 5,000 tonnes. By analysing how operating theatres were used and clearing bottlenecks, Newton enabled one NHS trust to treat 1,500 more patients each year.

People at Newton never start out assuming they know the answers – but they're always certain they'll find them. By uncovering the data so the most important decisions are made with facts, not opinions. By bringing together colleagues who are driven to make a real and meaningful impact. By creating a communal experience that inspires them to learn from each other. And by embedding into client organisations the same passion, self-belief and know-how that will enable them to take on any challenges in the future.

Newton's people drive the business. Their curiosity and tenacity, technical and problem-solving skills, and ability to communicate with colleagues and clients are what set the firm apart. And for its graduates, that difference can shape a career that's never not challenging. Never not inspiring. Never not Newton.

GRADUATE VACANCIES IN 2022
CONSULTING

NUMBER OF VACANCIES
135 graduate jobs

LOCATIONS OF VACANCIES

STARTING SALARY FOR 2022
£45,000-£50,000 package
Plus a sign-on bonus, company car, profit share bonus, and subsidised weekends away.

UNIVERSITY PROMOTIONS DURING 2021-2022
BATH, BIRMINGHAM, BRISTOL, CAMBRIDGE, DURHAM, EDINBURGH, EXETER, IMPERIAL COLLEGE LONDON, LONDON SCHOOL OF ECONOMICS, MANCHESTER, NOTTINGHAM, OXFORD, ST ANDREWS, STRATHCLYDE, UNIVERSITY COLLEGE LONDON, WARWICK
Please check with your university careers service for full details of Newton's local promotions and events.

MINIMUM ENTRY REQUIREMENTS
Any degree accepted

APPLICATION DEADLINE
23rd December 2021

FURTHER INFORMATION
www.Top100GraduateEmployers.com
Register now for the latest news, local promotions, work experience and graduate vacancies at Newton.

NEWTON

Ed, Digital Consultant

ARE YOU AS PASSIONATE ABOUT TECHNOLOGY AS ED IS?

Then a career in consulting could be right for you. We're Newton Europe, an operational improvement consultancy with a twist. Since 2001, we've delivered real and sustainable change to industries far and wide with the help of people like Ed. Recently, he built an AI based system for one of our clients in the defence sector, to help them better understand and evaluate the impact of the work they do. If you're looking to transform the lives of real businesses and real people, look no further.

Find out if a career in consulting is right for you at **WorkAtNewton.com**

NEVER NOT NEWTON

local.gov.uk/ngdp

ngdp.support@local.gov.uk

linkedin.com/company/ngdp-lga twitter.com/ngdp_LGA

GRADUATE VACANCIES IN 2022

GENERAL MANAGEMENT

NUMBER OF VACANCIES
150+ graduate jobs

LOCATIONS OF VACANCIES

STARTING SALARY FOR 2022
£25,991+
*Inner or outer London weighting
will be added where appropriate.*

**UNIVERSITY PROMOTIONS
DURING 2021-2022**
ASTON, BATH, BIRMINGHAM, BRADFORD,
BRISTOL, BRUNEL, CARDIFF, CITY, DURHAM,
ESSEX, EXETER, HULL, KEELE, KING'S
COLLEGE LONDON, KENT, LANCASTER,
LEEDS, LEICESTER, LIVERPOOL,
LONDON SCHOOL OF ECONOMICS,
LOUGHBOROUGH, MANCHESTER,
NEWCASTLE, NORTHUMBRIA, NOTTINGHAM,
NOTTINGHAM TRENT, PLYMOUTH, QUEEN
MARY LONDON, READING, ROYAL
HOLLOWAY, SHEFFIELD, SOUTHAMPTON,
SURREY, SUSSEX, UEA, UNIVERSITY
COLLEGE LONDON, WARWICK, YORK
*Please check with your university careers
service for full details of the NGDP's local
promotions and events.*

MINIMUM ENTRY REQUIREMENTS
2.2 Degree

APPLICATION DEADLINE
January 2022

FURTHER INFORMATION
www.Top100GraduateEmployers.com
*Register now for the latest news, local
promotions, work experience and
graduate vacancies at the NGDP.*

**The NGDP is a two-year programme which gives graduates
the opportunity and training to fast-track their career in local
government. Local government is responsible for providing
over 800 vital community services, and employs more than one
million people to deliver them.**

The NGDP exists to find and support the next generation of sector leadership.
It welcomes graduates motivated by a desire to lead in the public sector, whether
they are driven by a specific issue or more broadly want their work to have a
positive, tangible impact. Since its inception in 1999, the NGDP has brought
more than 1,400 new managers into local government.

NGDP graduate trainees make a real contribution to shaping and implementing
new ideas and initiatives from their first day. Each trainee is employed by a
participating council (or group of councils) for two years, during which time
they rotate between a minimum of three different placements across key areas
of the council. In the last year, NGDP trainees have pioneered digital inclusion
projects, refreshed their council's diversity and inclusion strategy, led climate
emergency initiatives, and become their borough's testing lead for COVID-19.
These are just a few examples of the placements in which NGDP trainees gain
valuable knowledge, experience, and transferrable skills, all of which make them
highly sought after in the public sector workforce.

The NGDP expects to recruit a cohort of at least 150 trainees next year,
placing each individual into a supportive community of peers. Councils provide
placement advisers and mentors for trainees, while the scheme's learning
programme develops trainees' management skills and deepens their knowledge
of the sector. Completion of the programme earns graduates a top-level
Institute for Leadership and Management qualification.

NHS
Graduate Management Training Scheme

graduates.nhs.uk

facebook.com/NHSGraduateScheme

instagram.com/NHSGraduateScheme   twitter.com/NHSGradScheme

linkedin.com/company/nhs-graduate-management-training-scheme

youtube.com/NHSGraduateManagementTrainingScheme

As Europe's largest employer, with an annual budget of over £100 billion, there is no other organisation on earth quite like the NHS. With the ability to have a positive impact on the health and wellbeing of 56 million people, the NHS Graduate Management Training Scheme is a life-defining experience.

Being on this scheme is unquestionably hard work, but this multi-award-winning, fast-track development scheme will enable graduates to become the healthcare leaders of the future. Graduates specialise in one of six areas: finance, general management, human resources, health informatics, policy & strategy, and health analysis.

As graduates grow personally and professionally, they'll gain specialist skills while receiving full support from a dedicated mentor at executive level. Every graduate joining the scheme will access a comprehensive learning and development package designed by some of the most experienced and expert learning providers in the UK. Success is granted only to those who are prepared to give their heart and soul to their profession.

The responsibility of the NHS demands that their future leaders have the tenacity, focus, and determination to deliver nothing but the best. Because the scheme offers a fast-track route to a senior-level role, graduates will soon find themselves facing complex problems head-on and tackling high profile situations.

Working for the NHS means standing up to high levels of public scrutiny and having decisions closely inspected. Graduates who want to succeed will need to be thick-skinned, resilient, and able to respond to constant change. This is a career where the hard work and unfaltering commitment of graduates not only affects the lives of others, but will ultimately define their own.

GRADUATE VACANCIES IN 2022
ACCOUNTANCY
FINANCE
GENERAL MANAGEMENT
HUMAN RESOURCES

NUMBER OF VACANCIES
300 graduate jobs

LOCATIONS OF VACANCIES

STARTING SALARY FOR 2022
£24,628

UNIVERSITY PROMOTIONS DURING 2021-2022
ASTON, BELFAST, BIRMINGHAM, BRADFORD, BRISTOL, DURHAM, EDINBURGH, EXETER, GLASGOW, HULL, LANCASTER, LEEDS, LEICESTER, LIVERPOOL, LOUGHBOROUGH, MANCHESTER, NEWCASTLE, NOTTINGHAM, READING, SHEFFIELD, STRATHCLYDE, SURREY, WARWICK, YORK
Please check with your university careers service for full details of the NHS's local promotions and events.

MINIMUM ENTRY REQUIREMENTS
2.2 Degree

APPLICATION DEADLINE
Year-round recruitment
Early application is advised.

FURTHER INFORMATION
www.Top100GraduateEmployers.com
Register now for the latest news, local promotions, work experience and graduate vacancies at the NHS.

Graduate Management Training Scheme

What impact could you make?

The NHS Graduate Management Training Scheme is nothing less than a life-defining experience. Whether you join our finance, general management, health analysis, health informatics, human resources, or policy and strategy scheme, you'll receive everything you need to make a positive impact on the lives of 56 million people across England.

These aren't clinical opportunities, but this is about developing exceptional healthcare leaders. High-calibre management professionals who will lead the NHS through a profound transformation and shape our services around ever-evolving patient needs. Inspirational people who will push up standards, deliver deeper value for money and continue the drive towards a healthier nation.

Visit:
www.nhsgraduates.co.uk

P&G

FRESH! AS IF DRIED OUTSIDE

P&G is one of the world's largest consumer goods companies, with employees from over 140 countries, and operations in approximately 70 countries. P&G aspires to build a better world – with equal voice and equal representation for everyone, and by being a leader in environmental sustainability.

A graduate role at P&G means starting a real job with real responsibility, straight out of university. Whether new joiners are students, graduates, or experienced professionals, they won't experience any rotational programmes or gradual onboarding here. Instead, from Day 1, they'll be able to dive into the meaningful work that makes an impact on P&G's leading brands, the world, and their careers. P&G invests heavily into the early development of their talents as they promote from within their own ranks, continuously aiming to grow the skills of their employees.

P&G offers a creative and dynamic work environment where their employees are at the core of everything they do. Whether helping to design their latest front-end innovation, selling to some of the UK and Ireland's biggest retailers, or designing a full-blown product launch, P&G employees will be empowered to succeed.

Most of all, P&G strives to represent the diversity of the consumers they serve. With around 60 nationalities represented in their Northern Europe workforce, their own diversity helps them to understand and meet the varied needs of consumers around the world.

All of which enables them to constantly challenge the status quo! From redesigning products (e.g. H&S beach plastic bottles) to implementing wholly new business models (e.g. loop), to using their voice in marketing to address important issues such as gender equality (e.g. "The best men can be", "Like A Girl"), and equality & inclusion (e.g. "The Words Matter", "Love Over Bias").

GRADUATE VACANCIES IN 2022
ENGINEERING
FINANCE
LOGISTICS
MARKETING
RESEARCH & DEVELOPMENT
SALES
TECHNOLOGY

NUMBER OF VACANCIES
50 graduate jobs

LOCATIONS OF VACANCIES

Vacancies also available in Europe.

STARTING SALARY FOR 2022
£Competitive

WORK EXPERIENCE
| DEGREE PLACEMENTS | SUMMER INTERNSHIPS |

UNIVERSITY PROMOTIONS DURING 2021-2022
ABERDEEN, ASTON, BATH, BIRMINGHAM, BRISTOL, BRUNEL, CAMBRIDGE, CARDIFF, DURHAM, EDINBURGH, EXETER, GLASGOW, IMPERIAL COLLEGE LONDON, KING'S COLLEGE LONDON, KENT, LANCASTER, LEEDS, LEICESTER, LIVERPOOL, LSE, LOUGHBOROUGH, MANCHESTER, NEWCASTLE, NORTHUMBRIA, NOTTINGHAM, NOTTINGHAM TRENT, OXFORD, OXFORD BROOKES, QMUL, SHEFFIELD, SOUTHAMPTON, ST ANDREWS, STRATHCLYDE, SUSSEX, UEA, UCL, WARWICK, YORK

MINIMUM ENTRY REQUIREMENTS
Varies by function
Relevant degree required for some roles.

APPLICATION DEADLINE
Varies by function

FURTHER INFORMATION
www.Top100GraduateEmployers.com
Register now for the latest news, local promotions, work experience and graduate vacancies at P&G.

Do something that matters from Day 1

To learn more about a career at P&G visit **pgcareers.com**

GRADUATE VACANCIES IN 2022

MARKETING

MEDIA

SALES

NUMBER OF VACANCIES
200+ entry-level roles

LOCATIONS OF VACANCIES

STARTING SALARY FOR 2022
£24,000

WORK EXPERIENCE

SUMMER INTERNSHIPS

UNIVERSITY PROMOTIONS DURING 2021-2022
Please check with your university careers service for full details of Penguin Random House's local promotions and events.

APPLICATION DEADLINE
Year-round recruitment

FURTHER INFORMATION
www.Top100GraduateEmployers.com
Register now for the latest news, local promotions, work experience and graduate vacancies at Penguin.

Penguin Random House UK connects the world with the stories, ideas, and writing that matter. As the biggest publisher in the UK, the diversity of its publishing includes brands such as Jamie Oliver, James Patterson, and Peppa Pig through to literary prize winners such as Zadie Smith and Richard Flanagan.

Career opportunities range from the creative teams in Editorial, Marketing, Publicity, and Design through to teams in Digital, Finance, Technology, Sales, and Publishing Operations, to name but a few.

The Scheme is Penguin Random House's flagship entry-level programme which offers 6-month traineeships to applicants who are Black, Asian, or from Minority Ethnic backgrounds and/or low socioeconomic backgrounds.

They also run 8-week Summer Internships that are open to all and offer the chance to work in teams from all departments: editorial, marketing, sales, and technology. For any vacancies or entry level programmes, there is no degree or educational requirement.

Penguin Random House has nine publishing houses – each distinct, with their own imprints, markets, and identity – including a fast-growing Audio publishing division.

They work with a wide range of talent: from storytellers, animators, and developers to entrepreneurs, toy manufacturers, producers, and – of course – writers. Just like broadcasters, they find increasingly different ways to bring stories and ideas to life.

Penguin Random House UK has two publishing sites in London – Vauxhall Bridge Road and Embassy Gardens; distribution centres in Frating, Grantham, and Rugby; and a number of regional offices. They employ over 2,000 people in the UK.

Your Story Starts Here

Finding a great story - editor, publisher, sales director, finance team. Making it look good - designer, copy writer, art director, illustrator. Making the finished book - production controller, product manager, quality controller. Getting it out there - marketing assistant, publicity manager, sales executive, social media manager.

Come and be part of the first of a new kind of publisher that captures the attention of the world through the stories, ideas and writing that matter.

Penguin
Random House
UK

GRADUATE VACANCIES IN 2022

ENGINEERING

LOGISTICS

MARKETING

SALES

NUMBER OF VACANCIES
15+ graduate jobs

LOCATIONS OF VACANCIES

STARTING SALARY FOR 2022
£30,000

WORK EXPERIENCE

| DEGREE PLACEMENTS | SUMMER INTERNSHIPS |

UNIVERSITY PROMOTIONS DURING 2021-2022
ASTON, BATH, BIRMINGHAM, BRISTOL, CARDIFF, DURHAM, EDINBURGH, EXETER, GLASGOW, IMPERIAL COLLEGE LONDON, KING'S COLLEGE LONDON, KENT, LANCASTER, LEEDS, LEICESTER, LIVERPOOL, LONDON SCHOOL OF ECONOMICS, LOUGHBOROUGH, MANCHESTER, NEWCASTLE, NOTTINGHAM, QUEEN MARY LONDON, READING, SOUTHAMPTON, SURREY, SUSSEX, UEA, UNIVERSITY COLLEGE LONDON, YORK
Please check with your university careers service for full details of PepsiCo's local promotions and events.

MINIMUM ENTRY REQUIREMENTS
Any degree accepted

APPLICATION DEADLINE
Late October 2021

FURTHER INFORMATION
www.Top100GraduateEmployers.com
Register now for the latest news, local promotions, work experience and graduate vacancies at **PepsiCo**.

PepsiCo is on a mission to create more smiles with every sip and bite with some of the world's favourite brands, such as Walkers, Pepsi Max, Quaker, Tropicana, Doritos, and Naked – to name just a few! PepsiCo UK has over 4,500 employees which are spread across ten UK sites.

PepsiCo's vision is to Be the Global Leader in Convenient Foods and Beverages by Winning with Purpose. Behind this vision lies a passion for sustainability and a commitment to doing business in the right way.

The team at PepsiCo are a hub of brilliant minds, creative disruptors and passionate individuals doing their bit to make difference in the world (they also quite like crisps). PepsiCo was built on entrepreneurship, autonomy, authenticity, and with customers at the heart, and these values still hold true today.

PepsiCo's graduate programme gives real-world challenges with real-world opportunities to shape trends and change the course of tomorrow. It is designed to help graduates build a foundation that can take them anywhere. Graduates will build a greater understanding of the business and cross-functional experience through rotations over three years.

From day one, PepsiCo graduates work on projects that matter. They shake things up, shape trends, and get guidance and development to help them discover their potential. They also manage projects that matter, receive world-class training, get coaching from senior leaders, and get a chance to test great ideas on global brands.

PepsiCo graduates are continually taking on new challenges. Introducing new products. Delivering surprising moments. Testing new Channels. Creating what's next. Take a look at PepsiCo's socials to find out more and apply today!

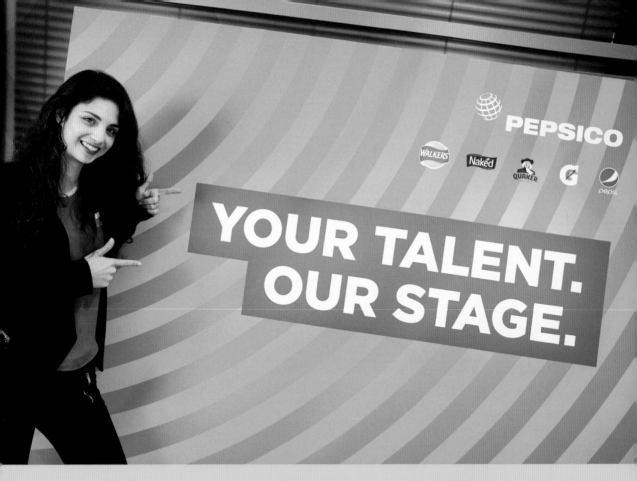

At PepsiCo, you get the best of both worlds: an entrepreneur's mindset plus reach and resources.

Bring your unique perspective. Bring curiosity. Bring ingenuity, and drive.

We'll give you a platform to be daring on a global scale.

www.pepsicojobs.com/student-uk-ireland

POLICE:NOW
INFLUENCE FOR GENERATIONS

facebook.com/PoliceNow   graduates@policenow.org.uk
linkedin.com/company/police-now   twitter.com/Police_Now
instagram.com/PoliceNowGraduates   youtube.com/PoliceNowChangeTheStory

Police Now is a charity with a mission to transform communities by recruiting, developing, and inspiring diverse leaders in policing. Diversity and inclusion matters; therefore, they aim to recruit high-achieving graduates from diverse backgrounds, especially those who might not have previously considered policing.

Since 2015, Police Now has recruited, trained, and developed over 2,000 police officers, posting them in neighbourhood roles in some of England and Wales' most deprived communities. Their outstanding participants play an important role in supporting the nation's police in their efforts to increase the number of officers across England and Wales and to drive positive change. It is important to have police officers as diverse as the communities that they serve, across the nation, and they have made it their mission to push this agenda.

Police Now's National Graduate Leadership Programme offers a career opportunity like no other. As a neighbourhood police officer, graduates will develop leadership skills for life. They will be placed in a unique and challenging environment, where they will make a real and lasting difference to some of the most vulnerable communities in England and Wales.

Throughout the two-year programme, they will be visible leaders in their community. They will develop skills in negotiation, problem-solving, decision-making, and emotional intelligence in their role as neighbourhood police officers.

At the end of the two years, they will have a number of exciting opportunities waiting for them. They'll be able to continue in a neighbourhood policing role, move to one of the other vast arrays of roles within policing, apply to join the National Policing Fast Track Programme run by the College of Policing, or leave policing altogether. Whichever pathway they choose, Police Now is an ever-growing family for which they will be an ambassador and alumni member.

GRADUATE VACANCIES IN 2022
POLICING

NUMBER OF VACANCIES
400+ graduate jobs

LOCATIONS OF VACANCIES

STARTING SALARY FOR 2022
£23,091
Average starting salary for 2021 cohort.

UNIVERSITY PROMOTIONS DURING 2021-2022
BATH, BIRMINGHAM, BRISTOL, CAMBRIDGE, CARDIFF, ESSEX, IMPERIAL COLLEGE LONDON, KEELE, KING'S COLLEGE LONDON, KENT, LANCASTER, LEEDS, LEICESTER, LIVERPOOL, LOUGHBOROUGH, MANCHESTER, NEWCASTLE, NORTHUMBRIA, NOTTINGHAM, NOTTINGHAM TRENT, OXFORD, READING, SHEFFIELD, SOUTHAMPTON, SURREY, SUSSEX, WARWICK, YORK
Please check with your university careers service for full details of Police Now's local promotions and events.

MINIMUM ENTRY REQUIREMENTS
2.2 Degree

APPLICATION DEADLINE
March 2022

FURTHER INFORMATION
www.Top100GraduateEmployers.com
*Register now for the latest news, local promotions, work experience and graduate vacancies at **Police Now**.*

BE THE
CHANGE

Society needs talented neighbourhood police officers as diverse as the communities they serve. Are you ready to lead change so that even the most vunerable can thrive?

To find out more, register your interest for Police Now's National Graduate Programme today.

Join us. Change the story.
policenow.org.uk

POLICE:NOW

INFLUENCE FOR GENERATIONS

Police Now is proud that of its 356 offer holders on the 2021 cohort, 54% identify as female, 46% male, 26% are of Black, Asian or Minority Ethnic heritage and 10% identify as LGBT+.

❚❚ We need people like you to represent the people we are policing.

LATIA SUEN
NEIGHBOURHOOD POLICE OFFICER

Find where you belong.

pwc

PwC's purpose is to build trust in society and solve important problems. Helping clients and communities address the biggest challenges they face has never been more important. Join Actuarial, Audit, Consulting, Deals, Legal, Risk, Tax, or Technology.

PwC's global strategy, called The New Equation, brings its purpose to life by bringing its people together to solve problems, often in unexpected ways, to reflect the unique challenges of modern times.

PwC employs 24,000 people across the UK, and attracting and retaining the best people is critical – as is empowering those people with technology and the opportunity to work flexibly and be their best selves.

An inclusive culture with investment in people is central to PwC's strategy. In some areas, this could mean working towards a professional qualification. In return, PwC ask that new joiners are eager to learn, with business awareness, intellectual and cultural curiosity, and the ability to build strong relationships. Graduates will be encouraged to work together, share knowledge and insights that foster innovation, drive impact, and deliver quality to clients.

Graduates and undergraduates can expect to be part of a stimulating environment, working on challenging projects in a culture that embraces difference. Their uniqueness and innovation is valued at PwC, which is why they have introduced a new Deal for all employees that ensures the experience of working there is right for everyone. Their hard work and accomplishments will be recognised and rewarded with a competitive salary and tailored, flexible benefits.

Bringing human-led, tech-powered innovations from concept to reality. Be a part of The New Equation.

GRADUATE VACANCIES IN 2022

ACCOUNTANCY

CONSULTING

FINANCE

LAW

TECHNOLOGY

NUMBER OF VACANCIES
Around 1,200 graduate jobs

LOCATIONS OF VACANCIES

STARTING SALARY FOR 2022
£Competitive

WORK EXPERIENCE

| INSIGHT COURSES | DEGREE PLACEMENTS | SUMMER INTERNSHIPS |

UNIVERSITY PROMOTIONS DURING 2021-2022
ABERDEEN, ABERYSTWYTH, ASTON, BANGOR, BATH, BELFAST, BIRMINGHAM, BRADFORD, BRISTOL, BRUNEL, CAMBRIDGE, CARDIFF, CITY, DUNDEE, DURHAM, EDINBURGH, ESSEX, EXETER, GLASGOW, HERIOT-WATT, HULL, IMPERIAL COLLEGE LONDON, KEELE, KING'S COLLEGE LONDON, KENT, LANCASTER, LEEDS, LEICESTER, LIVERPOOL, LSE, LOUGHBOROUGH, MANCHESTER, NEWCASTLE, NORTHUMBRIA, NOTTINGHAM, NOTTINGHAM TRENT, OXFORD, OXFORD BROOKES, PLYMOUTH, QMUL, READING, ROYAL HOLLOWAY, SOAS, SHEFFIELD, SOUTHAMPTON, ST ANDREWS, STIRLING, STRATHCLYDE, SURREY, SUSSEX, SWANSEA, UEA, ULSTER, UCL, WARWICK, YORK

MINIMUM ENTRY REQUIREMENTS
2.1 Degree

APPLICATION DEADLINE
Varies by function

FURTHER INFORMATION
www.Top100GraduateEmployers.com
Register now for the latest news, local promotions, work experience and graduate vacancies at PwC.

A community of solvers
addressing the biggest challenges
for business and society

Our purpose is to build trust in society and solve important problems.
Helping clients and communities address the biggest challenges they face
has never been more important. Our global strategy, called The New Equation,
brings our purpose to life by bringing our people together to solve problems,
often in unexpected ways to reflect the unique challenges of our times.
Developing our people is fundamental to our inclusive culture where your
uniqueness and innovation is valued and fresh ideas and new perspectives
are powered by the latest technology.

Bringing human-led, tech-powered innovations from concept to reality.
Be a part of The New Equation.

Learn more at *pwc.co.uk/TheNewEquation*

pwc

GRADUATE VACANCIES IN 2022

ENGINEERING
GENERAL MANAGEMENT
TECHNOLOGY

NUMBER OF VACANCIES
No fixed quota

LOCATIONS OF VACANCIES

STARTING SALARY FOR 2022
£28,500

UNIVERSITY PROMOTIONS DURING 2021-2022
Please check with your university careers service for full details of Rolls-Royce's local promotions and events.

MINIMUM ENTRY REQUIREMENTS
Varies by function
Relevant degree required for some roles.

APPLICATION DEADLINE
Year-round recruitment
Early application is advised.

FURTHER INFORMATION
www.Top100GraduateEmployers.com
Register now for the latest news, local promotions, work experience and graduate vacancies at Rolls-Royce.

Rolls-Royce pioneers cutting-edge technologies to sustainably meet the world's vital power needs. From building the world's most efficient large aero-engine to supporting NASA missions, Rolls-Royce transforms the potential of technology. A career at Rolls-Royce means shaping the future.

Pioneers do things differently. So, a career at Rolls-Royce means challenging the status quo and continually re-shaping the human experience. And because different ways of thinking make for better, bolder ideas, candidates will be joining a diverse, global workforce dedicated to that mission.

As these changing times have brought tough challenges for all, Rolls-Royce believes that now is the time to act as one community and one business. That includes supporting, rewarding, recognising, developing, and empowering everyone in the organisation to thrive and succeed – from those who have been with Rolls-Royce for years to those who are soon to join.

For those soon-to-be joiners, there are graduate and internship opportunities for candidates from STEM and Business with STEM disciplines to join the team and build a rewarding career. It could be a career firmly rooted in collaboratively striving for the next big technological breakthrough, or it could be a career in leadership, keeping everyone motivated, passionate, and full of pioneering spirit.

People who do well at Rolls-Royce are people who are self-aware, agile, creative, innovative, bold, and passionate about what Rolls-Royce does. As do people who are open-minded, collaborative, and can bring fresh perspectives to enduring challenges.

A career at Rolls-Royce means learning from, and working with, brilliant minds, helping solve complex, fascinating problems, and shaping the future.

ROYAL NAVY

Throughout the course of history, a life at sea has always attracted those with a taste for travel and adventure; but there are plenty of other reasons for graduates and final-year students to consider a challenging and wide-ranging career with the Royal Navy.

The Royal Navy is, first and foremost, a fighting force. Serving alongside Britain's allies in conflicts around the world, it also vitally protects UK ports, fishing grounds, and merchant ships, helping to combat international smuggling, terrorism, and piracy. Increasingly, its 30,000 personnel are involved in humanitarian and relief missions; situations where their skills, discipline, and resourcefulness make a real difference to people's lives.

Graduates are able to join the Royal Navy as Officers – the senior leadership and management team in the various branches, which range from engineering, air, and warfare to medical, the Fleet Air Arm, and logistics. Starting salaries of at least £25,984 – rising to £31,232 in the first year – compare well with those in industry.

Those wanting to join the Royal Navy as an Engineer – with Marine, Weapon, or Air Engineer Officer, above or below the water – could work on anything from sensitive electronics to massive gas-turbine engines and nuclear weapons. What's more, the Royal Navy can offer a secure, flexible career and the potential to extend to age 50.

The Royal Navy offers opportunities for early responsibility, career development, sport, recreation, and travel which exceed any in civilian life. With its global reach and responsibilities, the Royal Navy still offers plenty of adventure and the chance to see the world, while pursuing one of the most challenging, varied, and fulfilling careers available.

GRADUATE VACANCIES IN 2022
ENGINEERING
FINANCE
GENERAL MANAGEMENT
HUMAN RESOURCES
LAW
LOGISTICS
MEDIA
RESEARCH & DEVELOPMENT
TECHNOLOGY

NUMBER OF VACANCIES
No fixed quota

LOCATIONS OF VACANCIES

Vacancies also available elsewhere in the world.

STARTING SALARY FOR 2022
£25,984

WORK EXPERIENCE
INSIGHT COURSES | DEGREE PLACEMENTS | SUMMER INTERNSHIPS

UNIVERSITY PROMOTIONS DURING 2021-2022
Please check with your university careers service for full details of the Royal Navy's local promotions and events.

MINIMUM ENTRY REQUIREMENTS
Relevant degree required for some roles.

APPLICATION DEADLINE
Year-round recruitment

FURTHER INFORMATION
www.Top100GraduateEmployers.com
Register now for the latest news, local promotions, work experience and graduate vacancies at the Royal Navy.

ROYAL NAVY

A CAREER THAT MAKES
A WORLD OF DIFFERENCE

A career in the Royal Navy is like no other. A job where no two days are the same, where you can challenge yourself and solve problems on the go. Plus, you get to travel the world, all while helping those that are in need.

For more information call 0345 607 5555
Visit royalnavy.mod.uk/careers

RSM is a leading provider of audit, tax, and consulting services to middle-market leaders, globally. With around 3,650 partners and staff in the UK, and access to 48,000 people in over 120 countries across the RSM network, they can meet their clients' needs wherever in the world they operate.

As one of the world's largest networks of audit, tax, and consulting firms, they deliver the big ideas and services that help middle-market organisations thrive. Their global network spans more than 120 counties, but their passion is always the same: to help their clients move forward with confidence.

At RSM, graduates will gain access to an impressive client list and discover some of the world's most dynamic companies. Their work cuts across more than 40 service areas and a broad range of sectors – anything from Premier League footballers and leading charities to FTSE 300 companies and major multinationals.

They are a fast-growing firm with big ambitions – they have a clear goal to become the first-choice adviser to the middle market, globally. This vision touches everything they do, motivating and inspiring them to become better every day.

When new joiners become part of the team, they'll discover a culture that celebrates fresh thinking and embraces change. RSM forged a new path, uniting 120 firms around the world under one global brand name.

Their team of highly skilled learning and development specialists are committed to the ongoing careers and personal development of all their people. They have a wide range of programmes that have been created to allow individuals to tailor their development and career progression to suit their needs and aspirations.

As a responsible employer, RSM has clear goals to develop their diverse workforce, support their employees, and make a positive contribution to their local communities. Help shape their journey.

GRADUATE VACANCIES IN 2022
ACCOUNTANCY
CONSULTING
FINANCE

NUMBER OF VACANCIES
390-400 graduate jobs

LOCATIONS OF VACANCIES

STARTING SALARY FOR 2022
£Competitive

WORK EXPERIENCE
| DEGREE PLACEMENTS | SUMMER INTERNSHIPS |

UNIVERSITY PROMOTIONS DURING 2021-2022
ABERDEEN, ABERYSTWYTH, ASTON, BATH, BELFAST, BIRMINGHAM, BRADFORD, BRISTOL, CARDIFF, DUNDEE, DURHAM, EDINBURGH, ESSEX, EXETER, GLASGOW, HERIOT-WATT, HULL, KEELE, KING'S COLLEGE LONDON, KENT, LANCASTER, LEEDS, LEICESTER, LIVERPOOL, LSE, LOUGHBOROUGH, MANCHESTER, NEWCASTLE, NORTHUMBRIA, NOTTINGHAM, NOTTINGHAM TRENT, OXFORD BROOKES, READING, SHEFFIELD, SOUTHAMPTON, SURREY, SUSSEX, SWANSEA, UEA, UCL, WARWICK, YORK

MINIMUM ENTRY REQUIREMENTS
112 UCAS points
280 UCAS points for those who passed exams before 2017.

APPLICATION DEADLINE
Year-round recruitment
Early application is advised.

FURTHER INFORMATION
www.Top100GraduateEmployers.com
Register now for the latest news, local promotions, work experience and graduate vacancies at RSM.

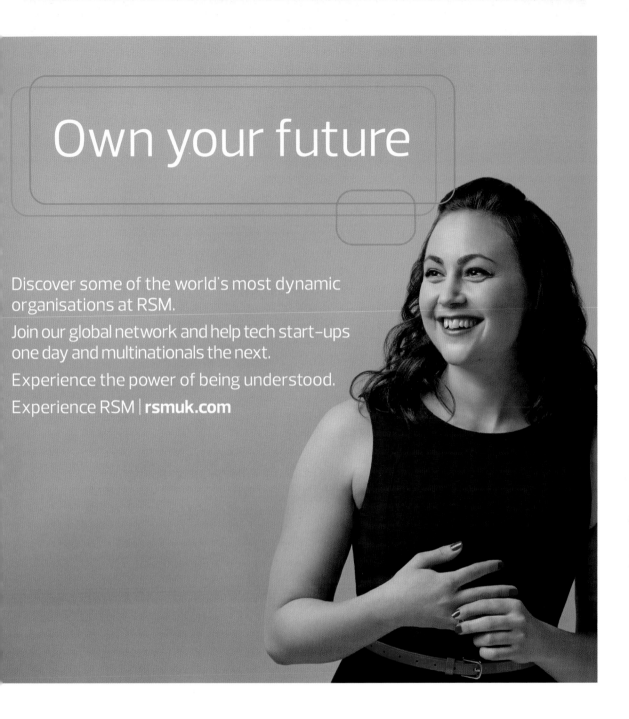

Own your future

Discover some of the world's most dynamic organisations at RSM.

Join our global network and help tech start-ups one day and multinationals the next.

Experience the power of being understood.

Experience RSM | **rsmuk.com**

THE POWER OF BEING UNDERSTOOD
AUDIT | TAX | CONSULTING

savills.co.uk/graduates

instagram.com/SavillsInstaGrad

Savills UK is a leading global real estate service provider listed on the London Stock Exchange. The company employs over 39,000 staff and has 600 offices and associates worldwide, providing all trainees with excellent scope for international experience as their careers develop.

Savills passionately believe that their graduates are future leaders, and as such make a huge investment in them. Savills graduates are given responsibility from day one, in teams that highly value their contribution, allowing them to be involved in some of the world's most high-profile property deals and developments. Graduates are surrounded by expert professionals and experienced team members from whom they learn and seek advice. Individual achievement is rewarded, and Savills look for bold graduates with entrepreneurial flair.

Savills are proud to have won *The Times Graduate Recruitment Award: Employer of Choice for Property* for the fifteenth year running. A great work-life balance, structured training, and a dynamic working environment are amongst the factors which see Savills nominated by final year students as the preferred Property employer year-on-year.

Savills' Graduate Programme offers the chance to gain an internationally recognised professional qualification. The company offers roles within Surveying, Planning, Sustainability, Food & Farming, and Forestry, and half of the Graduate Programme vacancies are positioned outside of London. The company has offices in exciting locations around the UK, where Fee Earners work with varied and prestigious clients. The diversity of Savills services means there is the flexibility to carve out a fulfilling, self-tailored career path in any location.

GRADUATE VACANCIES IN 2022
PROPERTY

NUMBER OF VACANCIES
80+ graduate jobs

LOCATIONS OF VACANCIES

STARTING SALARY FOR 2022
£23,500-£26,500
Plus a £500 sign-on bonus.

WORK EXPERIENCE

| INSIGHT COURSES | DEGREE PLACEMENTS | SUMMER INTERNSHIPS |

UNIVERSITY PROMOTIONS DURING 2021-2022
ABERDEEN, BATH, BIRMINGHAM, BRISTOL, CAMBRIDGE, CARDIFF, DURHAM, EDINBURGH, EXETER, GLASGOW, HERIOT-WATT, KING'S COLLEGE LONDON, LEEDS, LIVERPOOL, LONDON SCHOOL OF ECONOMICS, MANCHESTER, NEWCASTLE, NORTHUMBRIA, NOTTINGHAM TRENT, OXFORD, OXFORD BROOKES, READING, SHEFFIELD, UNIVERSITY COLLEGE LONDON, YORK
Please check with your university careers service for full details of Savills' local promotions and events.

MINIMUM ENTRY REQUIREMENTS
Any degree accepted
Relevant degree required for some roles.

APPLICATION DEADLINE
Mid November

FURTHER INFORMATION
www.Top100GraduateEmployers.com
Register now for the latest news, local promotions, work experience and graduate vacancies at Savills.

SHAPE YOUR FUTURE

"I was involved in high profile planning projects of between 2000 and 4000 homes within the first 6 months of joining Savills"

"I assisted with successfully pitching for the disposal of a portfolio of logistics assets across Northern Europe worth approximately €400 million"

"I have helped progress over 300 Megawatts of energy for the UK power grid through renewable developments - enough to power nearly 200,000 homes"

18
possible
career paths

2
year training programme
with permanent
employment contract

15
Years as The Times
Graduate Employer of
Choice for Property

40%
of our main board joined
as graduate trainees

39,000+
global employees

600+
offices in over
70 countries

A career in real estate offers an exciting and dynamic career path with the opportunity to specialise in several different areas that help shape the future of our built environment.

Become **the future of Savills**

@savillsinstagrad   #careersinproperty

shell.co.uk/careers

facebook.com/ShellUnitedKingdom **f**
linkedin.com/company/shell **in**   twitter.com/Shell **y**
instagram.com/Shell **O**   youtube.com/Shell **▶**

GRADUATE VACANCIES IN 2022

ENGINEERING
FINANCE
GENERAL MANAGEMENT
HUMAN RESOURCES
MARKETING
TECHNOLOGY

NUMBER OF VACANCIES
No fixed quota

LOCATIONS OF VACANCIES

Shell is an international energy company that aims to meet the world's growing needs for more, and cleaner, energy solutions in ways that are economically, environmentally, and socially responsible. It is one of the world's largest energy companies, operating in more than 70 countries.

The challenge for the future is to continue to meet growing global demand for energy at the same time as reducing carbon emissions. Shell has a global target to become a net zero emissions energy business by 2050, in step with society. This means that Shell aims to be net zero on all emissions generated by its operations and the energy needed to power them. The company is working with customers, businesses, and governments to address emissions across different sectors.

In the UK, Shell has been proud to play a vital role in finding and providing oil and gas for the UK for more than 120 years – helping to power industries, transport systems, and homes. They also offer home energy customers 100% renewable energy and have the largest network of charge points in the UK, ensuring customers can charge their cars at home, at work, and on the move.

At Shell, their interns and graduates can help drive innovation forward and develop tomorrow's energy solutions today. No matter their discipline, they will have the chance to work on meaningful projects that directly impact the business, whilst receiving training and support designed to nurture rock-solid career foundations. They will have the opportunity to power their careers to new heights and to be part of an inclusive culture that changes the global energy system and shapes the future.

Shell believes in creating an inclusive culture where their employees can thrive so, whatever their background or ambitions are, they can find and build their future at Shell.

STARTING SALARY FOR 2022
£Competitive

UNIVERSITY PROMOTIONS DURING 2021-2022
ABERDEEN, CAMBRIDGE, IMPERIAL COLLEGE LONDON, LEEDS, MANCHESTER, OXFORD, QUEEN MARY LONDON, STRATHCLYDE, UNIVERSITY COLLEGE LONDON, WARWICK
Please check with your university careers service for full details of Shell's local promotions and events.

APPLICATION DEADLINE
Varies by function

FURTHER INFORMATION
www.Top100GraduateEmployers.com
Register now for the latest news, local promotions, work experience and graduate vacancies at Shell.

THE FUTURE.
YOURS TO MAKE.

"I want to help people

My future is bringing energy to those in need"

Hayley
Engineer at Shell

Find out more at
shell.co.uk/careers

SIEMENS

Siemens is everywhere you look. Building the technologies that make the world move – reinventing mobility and smart infrastructure so cities, and even entire countries, flow autonomously. Its digital visionaries, multidisciplinary engineers, and business experts are forever learning.

Together, they've created a truly innovative and appealing community. Over 100 graduates and interns will experience Siemens' ultra-progressive, diverse culture and forward-thinking approach to the workplace. Not to mention tailored programmes that reflect students' interests and all the benefits that come with it. With Siemens' 'new normal' policy, they will be able to work from anywhere they want two to three days per week, depending on the type of role they are in.

Still, they can collaborate on innovative and prestigious projects worldwide – such as reimagining the iconic London Underground. Across the world, Siemens is building a future that's electrified, software-driven, and carbon-neutral. And its influence over global infrastructure really is here, there, and everywhere.

Inspired to build a truly moving future? Siemens' paid internships and graduate programmes challenge students to innovate, explore, and grow day after day on real-life mentor-guided engineering projects. Its world-class programmes empower grads and interns to influence significant projects from day one. Over two years, those undergoing early careers programmes develop the technical, interpersonal, and leadership skills needed to progress quickly and achieve more in their chosen career path. Siemens is looking for highly ambitious engineers and business-minded individuals studying degrees including: Software, Computer Science, Electrical & Electronic Engineering, Telecommunications, Manufacturing, Production, Automotive, and Business Support.

Ready to move beyond theory and build a future-defining era? The wait is over.

GRADUATE VACANCIES IN 2022
ENGINEERING
FINANCE
GENERAL MANAGEMENT
TECHNOLOGY

NUMBER OF VACANCIES
100+ graduate jobs

LOCATIONS OF VACANCIES

STARTING SALARY FOR 2022
£28,000

UNIVERSITY PROMOTIONS DURING 2021-2022
ASTON, BIRMINGHAM, LOUGHBOROUGH, MANCHESTER, NEWCASTLE, NOTTINGHAM, SHEFFIELD, SOUTHAMPTON
Please check with your university careers service for full details of Siemens' local promotions and events.

MINIMUM ENTRY REQUIREMENTS
2.1 Degree

APPLICATION DEADLINE
Late January 2022

FURTHER INFORMATION
www.Top100GraduateEmployers.com
Register now for the latest news, local promotions, work experience and graduate vacancies at Siemens.

Truly moving
futures here, there
and everywhere

It's time you moved beyond the theory and began
engineering a smarter, more connected future.

Learn more about graduate and internship opportunities
on our careers site: **siemens.co.uk/earlycareers**

SIEMENS

Sky is Europe's leading entertainment company. Every day Sky makes life easier and more enjoyable for over 24 million customers across six countries by connecting them with the best entertainment. How is this made possible? By a diverse and dedicated group of people who come from all walks of life.

Most people know Sky for its entertaining, dramatic, and action-packed shows, but what they may not realise is that nothing happens on screen without the talented people behind the scenes, working their magic. The team constantly beats tight deadlines, builds the latest tech, fights digital threats, and powers through brilliant projects every day.

Want to learn how to be a business leader? Develop cutting-edge products? Gain skills across the business, or become an expert in a specialist area? The range of graduate programmes at Sky gives new joiners the chance to do all this and more. They can contribute to world-renowned TV, cinema, sport, news, technology, broadband, and mobile.

Sky also offers insight days and summer internships to help graduates decide on a career that suits them best. From challengers to collaborators, Sky is always on the lookout for talented and diverse graduates who want to work in a fun, fast-moving environment. The business works hard to build an inclusive culture, where everyone can be themselves. Whoever they are. Wherever they're from. Surrounded by some of the best people in the industry. Benefiting from on-the-job learning. Enjoying the opportunity to try out new ideas and shape where the business goes next. They will also get to see and do things at Sky that they simply wouldn't experience anywhere else.

So, no matter which programme a graduate decides to join, they'll be at the heart of where the real action happens at Sky.

GRADUATE VACANCIES IN 2022

ACCOUNTANCY

CONSULTING

FINANCE

MARKETING

TECHNOLOGY

NUMBER OF VACANCIES
170+ graduate jobs

LOCATIONS OF VACANCIES

STARTING SALARY FOR 2022
£28,000-£35,000

WORK EXPERIENCE

INSIGHT COURSES | SUMMER INTERNSHIPS

UNIVERSITY PROMOTIONS DURING 2021-2022
BIRMINGHAM, BRADFORD, CITY, KING'S COLLEGE LONDON, LEEDS, QUEEN MARY LONDON
Please check with your university careers service for full details of Sky's local promotions and events.

MINIMUM ENTRY REQUIREMENTS
Any degree accepted

APPLICATION DEADLINE
Varies by function

FURTHER INFORMATION
www.Top100GraduateEmployers.com
Register now for the latest news, local promotions, work experience and graduate vacancies at Sky.

skyearlycareers.com

A League of Their Own
American Road Trip

Available on Demand

a sky original

Lights. Camera. Careers.

Sky Early Careers

Get ready to be inspired, get challenged,
develop expert skills and bold ambitions on
an action-packed Sky Early Careers Programme.

The **real action** happens off-screen

SLAUGHTER AND MAY/

slaughterandmay.com

trainee.recruit@slaughterandmay.com ✉

facebook.com/SlaughterandMayTraineeCareers

Slaughter and May is one of the most prestigious law firms in the world. The strength of their global practice is reflected both in the multi-jurisdictional nature of their work and their international client base. The firm is a trusted adviser to some of the largest global companies in the world.

There are distinct differences that set Slaughter and May apart from other global law firms. These differences are in relation to their international approach, multi-specialist training, and lack of billable targets.

Slaughter and May work with the very best law firms across the globe to support their clients, handpicked to meet the needs of each matter, to deliver integrated legal advice. Fundamental to their business model is the ability to work in partnership with other law firms – this is how they have built their successful global practice.

Slaughter and May lawyers are all trained to be multi-specialists across a broad range of legal matters. This is hard work, but their lawyers say it makes for a far more fulfilling career. It provides challenge and interest and also allows their lawyers to develop deeper relationships with clients, because they get to know their businesses better.

Their lawyers are not set billing targets. In this way, their lawyers are free to work collaboratively, sharing expertise and knowledge so that they can concentrate on what matters most – the quality of the work and client service.

Slaughter and May takes great store in drawing strength from diversity and believes that an inclusive workplace drives collaboration and enhances business performance. They are looking to employ the brightest minds regardless of what or where they studied. They offer open days, workshops, and work experience schemes to enable applicants to gain an insight into life as a commercial lawyer.

GRADUATE VACANCIES IN 2022
LAW

NUMBER OF VACANCIES
80 graduate jobs
For training contracts starting in 2024.

LOCATIONS OF VACANCIES

STARTING SALARY FOR 2022
£47,000

WORK EXPERIENCE
| INSIGHT COURSES | SUMMER INTERNSHIPS |

UNIVERSITY PROMOTIONS DURING 2021-2022
Please check with your university careers service for full details of Slaughter and May's local promotions and events.

MINIMUM ENTRY REQUIREMENTS
2.1 Degree

APPLICATION DEADLINE
Please see website for full details.

FURTHER INFORMATION
www.Top100GraduateEmployers.com
Register now for the latest news, local promotions, work experience and graduate vacancies at Slaughter and May.

SLAUGHTER AND MAY/

A WORLD OF DIFFERENCE

Laws, international markets, global institutions… all changing every day. So how do we, as an international law firm, create the agility of mind that enables us to guide some of the world's most influential organisations into the future?

By allowing bright people the freedom to grow. By training lawyers in a way that develops a closer understanding of clients through working on a wider range of transactions. By fostering an ethos of knowledge sharing, support and mutual development by promoting from within and leaving the clocks outside when it comes to billing. To learn more about how our key differences not only make a world of difference to our clients, but also to our lawyers and their careers, visit

slaughterandmay.com/careers

SLAUGHTER AND MAY/

80
Training Contracts

Lawyers from
67
universities

Worked with
230
law firms
globally in 2020

Teach First

teachfirst.org.uk/training-programme

facebook.com/TeachFirst [f]   recruitment@teachfirst.org.uk [✉]
linkedin.com/company/teach-first [in]   twitter.com/TeachFirst [✕]
instagram.com/TeachFirstUK [◉]   youtube.com/TeachFirstYT [▶]

Teach First is a charity fighting to end educational inequality. They develop brilliant teachers and leaders determined to make a difference in the schools facing the toughest challenges. Since 2002, 15,000+ trainees have helped change the lives of more than a million children from disadvantaged backgrounds.

Graduates have many career options ahead of them, but few are more meaningful than teaching. Too often, the future of a disadvantaged child is determined by their postcode, not their potential – they're 18 months behind their wealthier peers when they take their GCSEs, and this gap is growing wider still due to COVID-19. It's clear great teachers are needed – now more than ever – to help every young person get the education they deserve.

Teach First's Training Programme is the largest teacher training and leadership programme in the UK. It offers graduates a salary while they train and opens the door to a world of career possibilities. Over two years, they'll qualify as teachers and gain a fully funded Postgraduate Diploma in Education and Leadership (PGDE).

Through secondary, primary, or early years placements, trainees will make an instant impact on the lives of young people, in a role where no two days are the same. More than half of trainees continue teaching in schools after completing their PGDE, with the option of further support from Teach First to progress quickly into leadership roles. And the charity's influential network links them to organisations who value the diverse skills they bring.

The challenge is real, but so is the chance to create lasting change. With the most important generation of teachers and leaders, Teach First is fighting for a fairer future.

Visit the Teach First website to find out more and apply now.

GRADUATE VACANCIES IN 2022
TEACHING

NUMBER OF VACANCIES
1,750 graduate jobs

LOCATIONS OF VACANCIES

STARTING SALARY FOR 2022
£Competitive

WORK EXPERIENCE
INSIGHT COURSES

UNIVERSITY PROMOTIONS DURING 2021-2022
ABERDEEN, ABERYSTWYTH, ASTON, BANGOR, BATH, BELFAST, BIRMINGHAM, BRADFORD, BRISTOL, BRUNEL, CAMBRIDGE, CARDIFF, CITY, DURHAM, EDINBURGH, ESSEX, EXETER, GLASGOW, HERIOT-WATT, HULL, IMPERIAL COLLEGE LONDON, KEELE, KING'S COLLEGE LONDON, KENT, LANCASTER, LEEDS, LEICESTER, LIVERPOOL, LSE, LOUGHBOROUGH, MANCHESTER, NEWCASTLE, NORTHUMBRIA, NOTTINGHAM, NOTTINGHAM TRENT, OXFORD, OXFORD BROOKES, PLYMOUTH, QMUL, READING, ROYAL HOLLOWAY, SOAS, SHEFFIELD, SOUTHAMPTON, ST ANDREWS, SURREY, SUSSEX, SWANSEA, UEA, UCL, WARWICK, YORK

MINIMUM ENTRY REQUIREMENTS
2.1 Degree
However, all applications are assessed on a case-by-case basis.

APPLICATION DEADLINE
Year-round recruitment
Early application is advised.

FURTHER INFORMATION
www.Top100GraduateEmployers.com
*Register now for the latest news, local promotions, work experience and graduate vacancies at **Teach First**.*

Teach First

Spend your days watching

A. Clocks tick

B. Knowledge click

This is your chance to change the future. Join the most important generation of teachers and leaders to transform countless lives – starting with your own.

Apply now for our Training Programme

TESCO

tesco-careers.com/programmes

apprenticeshipandgraduaterecruitment@tesco.com

Tesco is a team of 360,000 colleagues, and has stores in the UK, Republic of Ireland, Czech Republic, Hungary, and Slovakia. As a leading multinational retailer, it aims to serve customers every day with affordable, healthy and sustainable food to help them enjoy a better quality of life and an easier way of living.

Tesco welcomes individuality and uniqueness. It wants colleagues to feel they can be themselves at work and it's committed to helping them be at their best. Tesco is building an inclusive workplace – a place to actively celebrate the cultures, personalities, and preferences of its colleagues who share the same purpose: to serve customers a little better every day – and graduates have a vital part to play.

Graduates are given responsibility from day one, so they can gain confidence in their role through hands-on experience. They have access to a wide variety of workshops and resources, online or at Heart – the on-site training academy – to help them develop skills like building their network, adaptable thinking, and leading change, as well as looking after their wellbeing. They'll be supported throughout the graduate programme by their manager and their buddy, who remember what it's like to be new.

As well as specialist programmes in Finance, Retail, and Technology, Tesco offers a generalist Business programme, with the opportunity to work in two different parts of the business. Whatever their role, Tesco graduates will be making a positive difference to customers, colleagues, and communities.

Graduates will gain a breadth of experience that will help them to think about their future at Tesco, beyond their programme, as there's a wide variety of job opportunities. As they finish their programme, graduates should be well-equipped to excel in a role that plays to their unique strengths and interests.

GRADUATE VACANCIES IN 2022

FINANCE
GENERAL MANAGEMENT
HUMAN RESOURCES
LOGISTICS
MARKETING
PROPERTY
PURCHASING
RETAIL
TECHNOLOGY

NUMBER OF VACANCIES
100+ graduate jobs

LOCATIONS OF VACANCIES

STARTING SALARY FOR 2022
£28,000-£32,000

WORK EXPERIENCE
SUMMER
INTERNSHIPS

UNIVERSITY PROMOTIONS DURING 2021-2022
KING'S COLLEGE LONDON, LEICESTER, LOUGHBOROUGH, QUEEN MARY LONDON, UNIVERSITY COLLEGE LONDON
Please check with your university careers service for full details of Tesco's local promotions and events.

MINIMUM ENTRY REQUIREMENTS
2.2 Degree

APPLICATION DEADLINE
Varies by function

FURTHER INFORMATION
www.Top100GraduateEmployers.com
*Register now for the latest news, local promotions, work experience and graduate vacancies at **Tesco**.*

Be yourself.

Become part of an inclusive culture that welcomes individuality and uniqueness. Apply for our fresh crop of opportunities in Business, Finance, Retail and Technology.

To find out more and apply, visit
tesco-careers.com/programmes

THG

thg.com

graduates@thg.com

instagram.com/thg   linkedin.com/company/thgplc

THG is a fast-moving, global technology business that specialises in taking brands direct to consumers. It has a portfolio of own brands including Myprotein and LOOKFANTASTIC, powered by its propriety ecommerce solution, THG Ingenuity. Established in 2004, the Group's global revenue reached £1.6bn in 2020.

In 2020, the business listed on the London Stock Exchange in a record-breaking IPO, cementing its position as one of the UK's most exciting organisations. In the same year, THG created more than 3,000 new jobs and pledged a £10 million aid package during the COVID-19 pandemic to support local and international communities. Giving back is at the heart of THG, and this commitment is embedded across the business. THG employs more than 10,000 talented individuals, and its impressive growth is creating thousands of new roles every year.

Graduate roles are available across the board: from finance, marketing, and communications to technology, operations, and logistics. THG's key divisions – THG Beauty, THG Nutrition, and THG OnDemand – are home to global brands, while the Group's THG Experience division enables deeply experiential brand-building environments through its prestige events location portfolio.

THG's brands are powered by THG Ingenuity, the Group's proprietary ecommerce platform. THG Ingenuity also enables the digital growth of third-party clients, including Homebase, Elemis, and Nestlé, who benefit from the technology, infrastructure, and brand-building capabilities of this unique end-to-end D2C platform.

THG celebrates diversity and ambition, regardless of background, and will give graduate employees the freedom and support to reach their full potential. A graduate role with THG gives young, talented people the opportunity to turbocharge their career by joining a thriving global powerhouse.

GRADUATE VACANCIES IN 2022
FINANCE
MARKETING
TECHNOLOGY

NUMBER OF VACANCIES
250+ graduate jobs

LOCATIONS OF VACANCIES

STARTING SALARY FOR 2022
£23,000-£40,000
Starting salaries vary depending on job role.

WORK EXPERIENCE
INSIGHT COURSES | DEGREE PLACEMENTS | SUMMER INTERNSHIPS

UNIVERSITY PROMOTIONS DURING 2021-2022
BATH, BIRMINGHAM, BRISTOL, CAMBRIDGE, DURHAM, EDINBURGH, GLASGOW, IMPERIAL COLLEGE LONDON, KING'S COLLEGE LONDON, LANCASTER, LEEDS, LIVERPOOL, LONDON SCHOOL OF ECONOMICS, LOUGHBOROUGH, MANCHESTER, NEWCASTLE, NOTTINGHAM, NOTTINGHAM TRENT, OXFORD, SHEFFIELD, SOUTHAMPTON, ST ANDREWS, UNIVERSITY COLLEGE LONDON, WARWICK, YORK
Please check with your university careers service for full details of THG's local promotions and events.

MINIMUM ENTRY REQUIREMENTS
2.1 Degree
Relevant degree required for some roles.

APPLICATION DEADLINE
Year-round recruitment

FURTHER INFORMATION
www.Top100GraduateEmployers.com
Register now for the latest news, local promotions, work experience and graduate vacancies at THG.

THG

Push *limits.*
Break *boundaries.*
Make an *impact.*

Choose a career *less* ordinary.

Find out more about our
exciting career paths at
THG.com/careers

MYPROTEIN [PRO]

THE PRE-WORKOUT

RAINBOW CANDY

POWERED BY PHASETECH
TIME-RELEASE TECHNOLOGY

NET WT. 14.8oz (42ml)

ESPA
THE
CLEANSING MILK
LE LAIT NETTOYANT

MD
BRIGHTENING Moisturizer
SPF 30

MYPROTEIN   LOOKFANTASTIC   COGGLES   IWOOT   ⬡ GLOSSYBOX   THG INGENU!TY

The Think Ahead programme is a new route into social work for graduates and career-changers remarkable enough to make a real difference to people with mental health problems. The paid, two-year programme combines on-the-job learning, a Master's degree, and leadership training.

Mental health social workers use therapy, support, and advocacy to enable people to manage the social factors in their lives – like relationships, housing, and employment – to allow them to get well and stay well.

The Think Ahead programme focuses on adult community mental health teams, supporting people living with a wide variety of illnesses such as bipolar disorder, schizophrenia, and personality disorders. These are multi-disciplinary teams, usually within an NHS Trust, which can include social workers, nurses, support workers, occupational therapists, psychologists, and psychiatrists.

Participants on the programme begin their training with an intensive six-week residential over the summer. This prepares them for frontline work by giving them a grounding in approaches to mental health social work.

Following this training, participants work within NHS mental health teams in units of four. Each unit is led by a highly experienced Consultant Social Worker, and participants share responsibility for the care of the individuals they work with. Participants become professionally qualified in the second year of the programme and are then able to work more independently.

Throughout the programme there is regular training and time allocated for academic study. The programme culminates in a Master's degree in social work. Leadership training also takes place throughout the programme, supporting participants to become excellent social workers and to work towards leading change in the future.

GRADUATE VACANCIES IN 2022
SOCIAL WORK

NUMBER OF VACANCIES
160 graduate jobs

LOCATIONS OF VACANCIES

STARTING SALARY FOR 2022
£17,200
Tax-free training bursary outside London.

£19,100
Tax-free training bursary inside London.

WORK EXPERIENCE
SUMMER INTERNSHIPS

UNIVERSITY PROMOTIONS DURING 2021-2022
BIRMINGHAM, CAMBRIDGE, DURHAM, KING'S COLLEGE LONDON, LEEDS, LIVERPOOL, MANCHESTER, NOTTINGHAM, QUEEN MARY LONDON, SHEFFIELD, SOUTHAMPTON, UNIVERSITY COLLEGE LONDON, YORK
Please check with your university careers service for full details of Think Ahead's local promotions and events.

MINIMUM ENTRY REQUIREMENTS
2.1 Degree

APPLICATION DEADLINE
Year-round recruitment
Early application is advised.

FURTHER INFORMATION
www.Top100GraduateEmployers.com
Register now for the latest news, local promotions, work experience and graduate vacancies at Think Ahead.

Think Ahead has given me a deeper understanding of the impact that mental illness can have on individuals.

Jan, Edinburgh graduate
and Think Ahead participant

THINK
AHEAD

thinkahead.org

TPP is a global digital health company. With more than 7,600 organisations using their solutions to care for over 50 million patients, their software is used across all health and social care settings, including GPs, emergency departments, hospitals, and mental health services.

TPP are committed to helping tackle global health challenges and delivering the future of healthcare. Their technology helps improve people's lives across the world, whether it is scheduling immunisations for millions of children, allowing doctors to manage care for elderly patients, helping governments with the prevention of outbreaks, or developing new machine learning algorithms for the early diagnosis of disease.

TPP's cloud database is one of the largest in the world, processing a billion transactions daily – more than the London Stock Exchange and Visa combined.

In both 2017 and 2018, TPP were awarded the "Top Company for Graduates to Work For" by TheJobCrowd, and in 2021 they were named the "Top IT Development and Consulting" company to work for!

What makes TPP different from most graduate employers is that they want their new starters to feel empowered to voice their ideas from day one. There is no 'typical' TPP personality – they value a wide range of interests and backgrounds as essential to creating a diverse and talented team who can solve real-world problems every day. Ideally located in the hustle and bustle of Leeds, TPP is a great place for graduates to learn and begin their career in one of the UK's largest and fastest growing cities. With a plethora of cultural hotspots, restaurants, and bars of every kind, and striking countryside just a train ride away, Leeds has plenty to offer for everyone. The company provides excellent starting salaries, fantastic benefits, and outstanding annual pay reviews.

GRADUATE VACANCIES IN 2022

MARKETING
SALES
TECHNOLOGY

NUMBER OF VACANCIES
50+ graduate jobs

LOCATIONS OF VACANCIES

STARTING SALARY FOR 2022
£28,000-£50,000

WORK EXPERIENCE
DEGREE PLACEMENTS | SUMMER INTERNSHIPS

UNIVERSITY PROMOTIONS DURING 2021-2022
BATH, BIRMINGHAM, BRADFORD, BRISTOL, CAMBRIDGE, DURHAM, EDINBURGH, IMPERIAL COLLEGE LONDON, KING'S COLLEGE LONDON, LANCASTER, LEEDS, LIVERPOOL, LONDON SCHOOL OF ECONOMICS, MANCHESTER, NEWCASTLE, NOTTINGHAM, OXFORD, QUEEN MARY LONDON, ROYAL HOLLOWAY, SHEFFIELD, SOUTHAMPTON, ST ANDREWS, UNIVERSITY COLLEGE LONDON, WARWICK, YORK
Please check with your university careers service for full details of TPP's local promotions and events.

MINIMUM ENTRY REQUIREMENTS
Varies by function
Relevant degree required for some roles.

APPLICATION DEADLINE
Year-round recruitment
Early application is advised.

FURTHER INFORMATION
www.Top100GraduateEmployers.com
Register now for the latest news, local promotions, work experience and graduate vacancies at TPP.

SOLVE PROBLEMS.
SAVE LIVES.

Software
Developer: **£50k**

Business
Analyst: **£50k**

Technical
Engineer: **£50k**

Product Support
Specialist: **£28k**

Account
Manager: **£50k**

NO EXPERIENCE REQUIRED

www.tpp-careers.com

UBS offers a collaborative, international, and diverse working environment that rewards passion, commitment, and success. They are a team of more than 70,000 colleagues speaking over 150 languages, collaborating across all major financial centres in more than 50 countries.

UBS are looking for hard-working, ambitious, and highly analytical individuals to join their early careers programs, offering opportunities in Investment Bank, Asset Management, and Group Functions.

UBS are offering a four-day long Spring Insights Program for students who are considering a career in banking but unsure where to start. Through a combination of workshops, interactive skills sessions, project work and networking opportunities, students will explore the possibilities at UBS whilst engaging their skills.

UBS's 10-week Summer Internship Program offers the opportunity to enhance business knowledge (and network) with business series, community days, and case studies.

UBS are offering a 12-month Industrial Placement Program where students will gain invaluable experience working with a team of diverse people and will enhance their skills through on-the-job training. This is a unique opportunity to learn more about UBS's culture, their people, and their business.

UBS's Graduate Talent Program lasts between 18 and 24 months. Graduates will be directly involved in day-to-day operations, working with professionals and gaining first-hand experience of the business. As well as on-the-job learning, they will also be training on the financial markets, products, and other core business topics. Rotations are a key part of some of the programmes; by taking on other roles in related departments, graduates will gain a wider perspective of the bank.

GRADUATE VACANCIES IN 2022

CONSULTING
FINANCE
GENERAL MANAGEMENT
HUMAN RESOURCES
INVESTMENT BANKING
TECHNOLOGY

NUMBER OF VACANCIES
100+ graduate jobs

LOCATIONS OF VACANCIES

Vacancies also available worldwide.

STARTING SALARY FOR 2022
£Competitive
Plus a competitive bonus.

WORK EXPERIENCE

| INSIGHT COURSES | DEGREE PLACEMENTS | SUMMER INTERNSHIPS |

UNIVERSITY PROMOTIONS DURING 2021-2022
ABERDEEN, ASTON, BATH, BIRMINGHAM, BRISTOL, BRUNEL, CAMBRIDGE, CARDIFF, CITY, DUNDEE, DURHAM, EDINBURGH, ESSEX, EXETER, GLASGOW, IMPERIAL COLLEGE LONDON, KING'S COLLEGE LONDON, KENT, LANCASTER, LEEDS, LEICESTER, LIVERPOOL, LOUGHBOROUGH, LSE, MANCHESTER, NEWCASTLE, NORTHUMBRIA, NOTTINGHAM, NOTTINGHAM TRENT, OXFORD, OXFORD BROOKES, PLYMOUTH, QMUL, READING, ROYAL HOLLOWAY, SHEFFIELD, SOAS, SOUTHAMPTON, ST ANDREWS, STIRLING, STRATHCLYDE, SURREY, SUSSEX, UCL, WARWICK, YORK

MINIMUM ENTRY REQUIREMENTS
2.1 Degree

APPLICATION DEADLINE
Year-round recruitment
Early application is advised.

FURTHER INFORMATION
www.Top100GraduateEmployers.com
*Register now for the latest news, local promotions, work experience and graduate vacancies at **UBS**.*

Influencing what's possible to expand my potential.

#morethanourselves

Ready to unlock your full potential?

Here at UBS, we draw on our differences – who we are, what we've experienced and how we think – to come together and deliver advice and solutions for our clients and for society. When we work together, the result of our work is stronger. Each of us is more than one person.

Visit our site to discover more: ubs.com/careers

Digital evolutions. New market opportunities. Fresh product and service offerings. Ready to join a firm that never sits still? We're not waiting for the future, we are actively shaping it. Commonly passionate, curious and adaptable, we disrupt the norm and bring new value for our clients, every day.

UBS is proud to be an equal opportunities employer. We respect and seek to empower each individual and the diverse cultures, perspectives, skills and experiences within our workforce.

Unilever

careers.unilever.com/uk-graduates

facebook.com/UnileverCareersUK [f]
linkedin.com/company/unilever [in] twitter.com/ULCareersUK [y]
instagram.com/UnileverCareersUK [O] youtube.com/Unilever [▶]

Unilever is a leading consumer goods company who make many of the world's best loved brands: Hellmann's, Lynx, Magnum, Tresemmé, Dove, and Simple, to name a few. Unilever products help people look good, feel good, and get more out of life. Unilever's purpose is to make sustainable living commonplace.

Over two billion consumers use their products every day. Their vision is to be the global leader in sustainable business, and they demonstrate how their purpose-led, future-fit business model drives superior performance. Unilever is looking for talented graduates who can challenge the way things are done, bring new ideas to the table, and dare to make big decisions to help achieve this ambition.

Graduates can apply to one of the following areas: human resources, finance, supply chain, research & development, customer development, marketing, and technology management. The Unilever Future Leaders Programme is about making a big impact on the business. It is about growing iconic, market-leading brands from the first day and tapping into continuous business mentoring, excellent training, and hands-on responsibility.

Graduates will have the chance to help Unilever build a better business and a better world, whilst finding their purpose to be their best self. Graduates will have real responsibility from day one, an opportunity of becoming a manager after three years, and a great support network to see them develop and attain their future goals. Dependent on function, Unilever will support graduates in achieving Chartered status and qualifications.

Graduates employed with Unilever have a fantastic opportunity to gain a great head start in their career and to make a real difference to Unilever's business and the world.

GRADUATE VACANCIES IN 2022
ENGINEERING
FINANCE
HUMAN RESOURCES
LOGISTICS
MARKETING
RESEARCH & DEVELOPMENT
SALES
TECHNOLOGY

NUMBER OF VACANCIES
40+ graduate jobs

LOCATIONS OF VACANCIES

STARTING SALARY FOR 2022
£32,000
Plus a £5,000 interest-free loan, an annual bonus, and an annual salary increase.

WORK EXPERIENCE
DEGREE PLACEMENTS   SUMMER INTERNSHIPS

UNIVERSITY PROMOTIONS DURING 2021-2022
Please check with your university careers service for full details of Unilever's local promotions and events.

MINIMUM ENTRY REQUIREMENTS
Varies by function
Relevant degree required for some roles.

APPLICATION DEADLINE
Autumn 2021
Early application is advised.

FURTHER INFORMATION
www.Top100GraduateEmployers.com
Register now for the latest news, local promotions, work experience and graduate vacancies at Unilever.

CHANGE LED BY YOU

A better business.
A better world.
A better you.

JOIN NOW
unilever.com/careers/graduates

Unilever

Unlocked

GRADUATE VACANCIES IN 2022
PRISON OFFICER

NUMBER OF VACANCIES
130 graduate jobs

LOCATIONS OF VACANCIES

STARTING SALARY FOR 2022
£23,000-£31,000
Dependent on location.

WORK EXPERIENCE
SUMMER
INTERNSHIPS

UNIVERSITY PROMOTIONS DURING 2021-2022
ASTON, BATH, BIRMINGHAM, BRISTOL, BRUNEL, CAMBRIDGE, CARDIFF, DURHAM, EDINBURGH, ESSEX, EXETER, GLASGOW, IMPERIAL COLLEGE LONDON, KING'S COLLEGE LONDON, KENT, LANCASTER, LEEDS, LEICESTER, LIVERPOOL, LONDON SCHOOL OF ECONOMICS, LOUGHBOROUGH, MANCHESTER, NEWCASTLE, NOTTINGHAM, OXFORD, QUEEN MARY LONDON, ROYAL HOLLOWAY, SHEFFIELD, SOUTHAMPTON, SUSSEX, UEA, UNIVERSITY COLLEGE LONDON, WARWICK, YORK
Please check with your university careers service for full details of Unlocked's local promotions and events.

MINIMUM ENTRY REQUIREMENTS
2.1 Degree

APPLICATION DEADLINE
December 2021 - January 2022

FURTHER INFORMATION
www.Top100GraduateEmployers.com
*Register now for the latest news, local promotions, work experience and graduate vacancies at **Unlocked**.*

Unlocked Graduates is a unique two-year leadership development programme that puts brilliant graduates at the heart of prison reform. Nearly half of all adult prisoners reoffend within one year of leaving prison, creating more victims, untold damage, and a cost of over £18 billion.

The problems facing prisons are some of the most complex in society. That's the challenge at the heart of the Unlocked Graduates two-year leadership development programme. Unlocked looks for ambitious graduates who are passionate about shaping the system for the better – as well as gaining a fully funded bespoke Master's degree, a highly competitive salary, the mentorship of an experienced prison officer, unique experiences, and development opportunities with key employers.

Combining academic study with real-world experience, Unlocked provides the platform to trial and assess solutions within prisons. And, in their second year, graduates get to write and present a policy paper to the Ministry of Justice.

As a prison officer, no two days are the same. Helping some of the most vulnerable and challenging people in society means being prepared for new situations – and being an advocate, negotiator, diplomat, and leader. It calls for a calm head, confidence, and problem-solving skills – all of which graduates develop with Unlocked. With real responsibility from day one, it's the rare chance to learn how to expertly face challenges head-on and hone expertise in leadership and communication – whether on the prison landing or in the Governor's office.

Many graduates choose to stay within the justice system after the programme, but no matter where their career takes them, Unlocked supports a growing network of change-makers. Being a prison officer is about so much more than locking up. With Unlocked Graduates, it can really open doors.

RYAN, UNLOCKED GRADUATE.

THE BEST PART OF MY JOB?
HELPING PRISONERS ESCAPE.

unlockedgrads.org.uk

Unlocked Graduates is a unique two-year leadership programme that puts brilliant graduates at the heart of prison reform. Nearly half of all prisoners reoffend within a year, creating more victims, untold damage, and a cost of £18 billion.

As frontline prison officers across London, the South East, West Midlands and North West, Unlocked's graduates study a fully-funded master's degree in prison theory and leadership. They get access to major employers; have the opportunity to present new policies to the Ministry of Justice and, above all, have the chance to support prisoners to turn their lives around and lead system change from the inside.

Unlocked | Leading change on the inside

vodafone

As a global tech leader, Vodafone transforms lives and businesses around the world. From developing pioneering IoT technology to connecting 50 million unbanked people to financial services through smart phones, Vodafone connects millions of people to endless possibilities.

Vodafone's purpose is to build a digital society that enhances socio-economic progress, embraces everyone, and does not come at the cost of the planet. To support this and its 670 million customers, constant innovation underpins everything Vodafone does. When hit by a crisis, Vodafone takes action. With the impact of COVID-19, Vodafone set up a 'SIMs for schools' campaign to ensure all students affected by the digital divide were still able to access learning from home.

Graduates at Vodafone will be inspired to experiment, try new things, and make mistakes. After all, it's the fastest way to learn. Their Discover graduate programme allows talented young minds to gain hands-on experience, technical skills, personal and professional growth, and the opportunity to learn from industry experts – all at a company that's an industry game changer.

Graduates can make an impact in areas including Tech, Finance, Business, Commercial, and HR. It's a chance to be part of a global community of graduates that are revolutionising connectivity through technology and innovation.

Vodafone relies on innovators, challengers, those that think differently, who are adaptable, and who are not afraid to push the boundaries. All this helps Vodafone's graduates achieve their ambitious goals. Joining Vodafone means being part of a truly diverse and inclusive group of like-minded people who want to change the world.

Together we can.

GRADUATE VACANCIES IN 2022

FINANCE
GENERAL MANAGEMENT
HUMAN RESOURCES
SALES
TECHNOLOGY

NUMBER OF VACANCIES
150-200 graduate jobs

LOCATIONS OF VACANCIES

STARTING SALARY FOR 2022
£30,000-£33,000
Plus an annual bonus.

WORK EXPERIENCE
DEGREE PLACEMENTS   SUMMER INTERNSHIPS

UNIVERSITY PROMOTIONS DURING 2021-2022
ASTON, BATH, BIRMINGHAM, LEEDS, LOUGHBOROUGH, NOTTINGHAM, QUEEN MARY LONDON, UNIVERSITY COLLEGE LONDON, WARWICK
Please check with your university careers service for full details of Vodafone's local promotions and events.

MINIMUM ENTRY REQUIREMENTS
2.2 Degree

APPLICATION DEADLINE
Varies by function

FURTHER INFORMATION
www.Top100GraduateEmployers.com
*Register now for the latest news, local promotions, work experience and graduate vacancies at **Vodafone**.*

wellcome.ac.uk/graduates

jobs@wellcome.ac.uk

twitter.com/WellcomeTrust   facebook.com/WellcomeTrust **f**

youtube.com/WellcomeTrust ▶ linkedin.com/company/wellcome-trust **in**

Wellcome is a global charitable foundation, both politically and financially independent. Wellcome exists to improve health for everyone by helping great ideas to thrive. It supports researchers, takes on big health challenges, campaigns for better science, and helps everyone get involved with science and health research.

Wellcome supports transformative work, such as co-funding the development of an Ebola vaccine, campaigning to secure change in mitochondrial donation, and launching Wellcome Collection. In 2020, Wellcome supported global research efforts to overcome the COVID-19 pandemic.

As well as funding scientific and medical research, Wellcome works at the intersection of health and society, and so is looking for graduates from all backgrounds. For recent graduates, Wellcome offers two-year development programmes. The general programme gives experience of different jobs for six months each. These could involve working with Wellcome's Africa and Asia Programmes, writing parliamentary briefings, or finding ways to engage the public. Wellcome also offers career-specific programmes in areas like investments for those who are ready to specialise.

Whichever programme graduates choose, they'll be valued team members, with support from mentors, line managers, and peers. With a focus on development, the programmes encourage graduates to work outside of their comfort zone, to expand their potential.

At the end of the programmes many graduates go on to more senior roles at Wellcome, while others move to other charities, further study, cultural venues, or even setting up their own businesses. Whatever graduates choose, Wellcome values ongoing relationships with its alumni so they can continue to make a difference in global health.

GRADUATE VACANCIES IN 2022

GENERAL MANAGEMENT
HUMAN RESOURCES
INVESTMENT BANKING
MEDIA
RESEARCH & DEVELOPMENT
TECHNOLOGY

NUMBER OF VACANCIES
12 graduate jobs

LOCATIONS OF VACANCIES

STARTING SALARY FOR 2022
£26,000

WORK EXPERIENCE
SUMMER
INTERNSHIPS

UNIVERSITY PROMOTIONS DURING 2021-2022
BATH, BRISTOL, BRUNEL, CAMBRIDGE, CITY, KING'S COLLEGE LONDON, KENT, LANCASTER, LEEDS, LEICESTER, LONDON SCHOOL OF ECONOMICS, MANCHESTER, NOTTINGHAM, QUEEN MARY LONDON, READING, ROYAL HOLLOWAY, SCHOOL OF AFRICAN STUDIES, SHEFFIELD, ST ANDREWS, UEA, UNIVERSITY COLLEGE LONDON
Please check with your university careers service for full details of Wellcome's local promotions and events.

MINIMUM ENTRY REQUIREMENTS
2.2 Degree

APPLICATION DEADLINE
Varies by function

FURTHER INFORMATION
www.Top100GraduateEmployers.com
Register now for the latest news, local promotions, work experience and graduate vacancies at Wellcome.

wellcome

"One of the best things is being part of a community of other graduates who together form a network across the whole organisation and share ideas, experiences and knowledge from beyond our own specific roles"

Poppy, 2019 graduate

WHITE & CASE

whitecasetrainee.com

facebook.com/WhiteCase   londontrainee@whitecase.com
linkedin.com/company/white-&-case twitter.com/WhiteCase
instagram.com/WhiteCase youtube.com/WhiteCaseGlobal

White & Case is a global law firm of more than 2,500 lawyers worldwide. They've built an unrivalled network of 45 offices in 31 countries. That investment is the foundation for their client work in over 200 countries today. Many White & Case clients are multinational organisations with complex needs that require the involvement of multiple offices.

White & Case trainees will work on fast-paced, cutting-edge cross-border projects from the outset of their career. White & Case is looking to recruit ambitious trainees who have a desire to gain hands-on practical experience from day one and a willingness to take charge of their own career. They value globally minded citizens of the world who are eager to work across borders and cultures, and who are intrigued by solving problems within multiple legal systems.

The training contract consists of four six-month seats, one of which is guaranteed to be spent in one of their overseas offices.

They offer vacation scheme placements over the winter, spring, and summer, open days, and two-day insight schemes. These provide a great way to experience first-hand what life is like as a White & Case trainee as well as gain useful insight into the firm and the training they offer.

The firm's virtual learning programme offers the opportunity to gain first-hand insight into life as a White & Case trainee and experience the realities of cross-border law. There is no cost to access the platform, it is self-paced to fit around users' schedules, and no application form or legal knowledge is required. Students will gain insight into the fast-paced, cutting-edge projects their lawyers and trainees work on, and gain valuable skills by undertaking true-to-life legal tasks. Participation in the learning platform will be recognised on their application forms.

GRADUATE VACANCIES IN 2022
LAW

NUMBER OF VACANCIES
50 graduate jobs
For training contracts starting in 2024.

LOCATIONS OF VACANCIES

STARTING SALARY FOR 2022
£50,000

WORK EXPERIENCE
| INSIGHT COURSES | DEGREE PLACEMENTS | SUMMER INTERNSHIPS |

UNIVERSITY PROMOTIONS DURING 2021-2022
Please check with your university careers service for full details of White & Case's local promotions and events.

MINIMUM ENTRY REQUIREMENTS
2.1 Degree

APPLICATION DEADLINE
Please see website for full details.

FURTHER INFORMATION
www.Top100GraduateEmployers.com
*Register now for the latest news, local promotions, work experience and graduate vacancies at **White & Case**.*

Together we make a mark

Graduate careers in law

As a trainee in our London office, you will have the opportunity to work on challenging cross-border client matters providing you with international experience and exposure from day one. Join us and make your mark.

whitecasetrainee.com

1	**75**	**£50k**
of the only law firms to offer a guaranteed overseas seat	vacation scheme places per year in London	year-one trainee starting salary

45	**50**	**£130k**
offices across 31 countries	trainees recruited per year in London	salary on qualification

WHITE & CASE

Useful Information